# NEW National Cur Mathematics

## K. M. Vickers and M. J. Tipler

© K. M. Vickers, M. J. Tipler and H. L. van Hiele 1992, 1995

First published in 1992 by Canterbury Educational Ltd
Revised edition published in 1995 by:
Stanley Thornes (Publishers) Ltd
Ellenborough House, Wellington Street
CHELTENHAM, Glos. GL50 1YW
England

96  97  98  99  00  /  10  9  8  7  6  5  4  3  2

The right of K. M. Vickers, M. J. Tipler and H. L. van Hiele to be
identified as authors of this work has been asserted by them in
accordance with the Copyright, Designs and Patents Act 1988

A catalogue record for this book is available from the British Library

ISBN 0-7487-2868-6
ISBN 0-7487-2869-4  (with answers)

Printed and bound in Great Britain by
BPC Paulton Books Ltd, Paulton.

# PREFACE

**"National Curriculum Mathematics"** by K.M. Vickers and M.J. Tipler is a complete course carefully designed and now updated to ensure full coverage of the revised National Curriculum.

In the 1995 revised National Curriculum, the Level Descriptions describe the performance that pupils working at a particular level should demonstrate. This book covers all the material in **Level 4** of the National Curriculum in four separate sections: Number; Algebra; Shape, Space and Measures; and Handling Data. Using and Applying Mathematics is integrated throughout the book. The material is presented in this order to enable pupils, or a group of pupils, to work across the different areas of mathematics at different levels.

Each section begins with revision from previous levels, printed on pink paper for ease of identification. Each section ends with a review chapter which contains revision questions on the material developed in this book. In each of the other chapters, every skill developing exercise finishes with review questions.

With the exception of the Review chapters, all chapters begin with "Did You Know" and a discussion; and finish with either "Just For Fun" or a Project. Throughout each topic, relevance to everyday life is emphasised. The acquisition of knowledge and skills is integrated with the use and application of these skills and this knowledge.

This book does not replace the teacher. Rather, it is a resource for both the pupil and the teacher. The teacher can be flexible about what is taught and when.

Throughout the book there is a variety of activities: skill developing exercises, investigations, practical work, problem solving activities, discussion exercises, puzzles and games. All the activities are related to the topic being studied. Whenever possible, activities and exercises have been written as open rather than closed tasks.

There is a good balance between tasks which develop knowledge, skills and understanding, and those which develop the ability to tackle and solve problems. Many activities do both. There is a thorough and careful development of each topic. Questions within each exercise or activity are carefully graded to build pupil confidence.


This book takes into consideration:
>    pupils' needs
>    pupils' interests
>    pupils' experiences
>    the need for pupils to explore mathematics
>    the use of technology
>    both independent and co-operative work habits

This book encourages pupils to:
> use a wide range of mathematics
> discuss mathematical ideas
> undertake investigations
> participate in practical activities
> use reference material
> relate mathematics to everyday life
> select appropriate methods for a task
> analyse and communicate information
> discuss difficulties
> ask questions

It is hoped that the pupil who uses this book will:
> develop a real interest in mathematics
> become well motivated
> gain much enjoyment from mathematics
> develop a fascination with mathematics
> develop an ability to use mathematics in other subjects
> become confident in the use of the calculator and computer
> gain a firm foundation for further study
> become proficient at applying mathematics to everyday life
> develop both independent and co-operative work habits
> become aware of the power and purpose of mathematics
> develop an ability to communicate mathematics
> develop an appreciation of the relevance of mathematics
> develop an ability to think precisely, logically and creatively
> become confident at mathematics
> gain a sense of satisfaction

Calculator keying sequences are appropriate for most calculators.

The version of LOGO used is LOGOTRON—standard LOGO for the BBC. The version of BASIC used is BBC BASIC.

K.M. Vickers
1995

## Acknowledgements

The author wishes to thank all those firms and enterprises who have so kindly given permission to reproduce tables and other material. A special thanks to S. P. R. Coxon, I. Kelderman, J.A. Ogilvie and S. Napier for their valuable contributions; to F. Tunnicliffe for the illustrations and J. McClelland for the photographs.

Every effort has been made to trace all the copyright holders. If any have been inadvertently overlooked the publishers will be pleased to make the necessary arrangement at the first opportunity.

# Contents

## NUMBER

# ALGEBRA

# SHAPE, SPACE and MEASURES

# HANDLING DATA

# Level Descriptions for Level 4

## Attainment Target 1: Using and Applying Mathematics

● **Level 4**

Pupils are developing their own strategies for solving problems and are using these strategies both in working within mathematics and in applying mathematics to practical contexts. They present information and results in a clear and organised way, explaining the reasons for their presentation. They search for a pattern by trying out ideas of their own.

## Attainment Target 2: Number and Algebra

● **Level 4**

Pupils use their understanding of place value to multiply and divide whole numbers by 10 or 100. In solving number problems, pupils use a range of mental and written methods of computation with the four operations, including mental recall of multiplication facts up to $10 \times 10$. They add and subtract decimals to two places. In solving problems with or without a calculator, pupils check the reasonableness of their results by reference to their knowledge of the context or to the size of the numbers. They recognise approximate proportions of a whole and use simple fractions and percentages to describe these. Pupils explore and describe number patterns, and relationships including multiple, factor and square. They have begun to use simple formulae expressed in words. Pupils use and interpret co-ordinates in the first quadrant.

## Attainment Target 3: Shape, Space and Measures

● **Level 4**

Pupils make 3-D mathematical models by linking given faces or edges, draw common 2-D shapes in different orientations on grids, and identify congruent shapes and orders of rotational symmetry. They reflect simple shapes in a mirror line. They choose and use appropriate units and instruments, interpreting, with appropriate accuracy, numbers on a range of measuring instruments. They find perimeters of simple shapes, find areas by counting squares, and find volumes by counting cubes.

## Attainment Target 4: Handling Data

● **Level 4**

Pupils collect discrete data and record them using a frequency table. They understand and use the mode and median. They group data, where appropriate, in equal class intervals, represent collected data in frequency diagrams and interpret such diagrams. They construct and interpret simple line graphs. They understand and use simple vocabulary associated with probability, including 'fair', 'certain' and 'likely'.

# NUMBER

# Number from Previous Levels

## ADDITION and SUBTRACTION

Addition and subtraction, using numbers as large as 20, should be done mentally.

For instance, $14 + 9 = 23$
$19 - 7 = 12$
$18 + 0 = 18$

Mental calculations can sometimes be made easier by rewriting the numbers.

For instance,

$$23 + 34 = 20 + 3 + 30 + 4$$
$$= 20 + 30 + 3 + 4$$
$$= 50 + 7$$
$$= 57$$

$$29 - 8 = 30 - 1 - 8$$
$$= 30 - 9$$
$$= 21$$

## MULTIPLICATION and DIVISION

The multiplication facts, given in these two tables, should be known.

| × | 1 | 2 | 3 | 4 | 5 |
|---|---|---|---|---|---|
| 1 | 1 | 2 | 3 | 4 | 5 |
| 2 | 2 | 4 | 6 | 8 | 10 |
| 3 | 3 | 6 | 9 | 12 | 15 |
| 4 | 4 | 8 | 12 | 16 | 20 |
| 5 | 5 | 10 | 15 | 20 | 25 |

| × | 1 | 2 | 3 | 4 | 5 | 6 | 7 | 8 | 9 | 10 |
|---|---|---|---|---|---|---|---|---|---|---|
| 2 | 2 | 4 | 6 | 8 | 10 | 12 | 14 | 16 | 18 | 20 |
| 5 | 5 | 10 | 15 | 20 | 25 | 30 | 35 | 40 | 45 | 50 |
| 10 | 10 | 20 | 30 | 40 | 50 | 60 | 70 | 80 | 90 | 100 |

*continued . . .*

. . . *from previous page*

## PLACE VALUE

Place value is given by this chart:

| thousands | hundreds | tens | units (ones) |
|:---:|:---:|:---:|:---:|
| 2 | 3 | 4 | 7 |

For instance; in the number 2347, the digit 2 means 2 thousands
the digit 3 means 3 hundreds
the digit 4 means 4 tens
the digit 7 means 7 ones

## ROUNDING

27 is closer to 30 than to 20.          327 is closer to 300 than to 400.
27 rounded to the nearest 10 is 30.     327 rounded to the nearest 100 is 300.

45 is halfway between 40 and 50.
45 rounded to the nearest 10 is 50.

## CALCULATION

If 11 is divided by 5, the answer is 2 with remainder 1.

If we do the multiplication £1·35 × 4 on the calculator,
the display is 5·4.
The answer to the multiplication £1·35 × 4 is not
written as £5·4; it is written as £5·40.

| 5.4 |
|---:|

## NEGATIVE NUMBERS

Numbers less than zero are called **negative numbers.**
The number −4 is a negative number. −4 means 4 less than zero.

For instance, if a temperature is given as −4 °C, the temperature is 4° below
zero.

*continued . . .*

*. . . from previous page*

## FRACTIONS

$\frac{1}{2}$ of these are red. $\frac{1}{4}$ are grey.

## PATTERNS

The **even** numbers are 2, 4, 6, 8, . . .
The **odd** numbers are 1, 3, 5, 7, . . .

The . . . indicates that the pattern continues.

## SYMBOLS

**Symbols** may be used to stand for a number.

For instance,    in 3 + ★ = 7 the ★ stands for 4
                 in 5 – 2 = □ the □ stands for 3.

< means "is less than". For instance   17 < 20.
> means "is greater than". For instance   5 > 4.

## REVISION EXERCISE

1. Write these numbers using digits.    (a)   four hundred and two

                                       (b)   four thousand and thirty

2. What number goes in each box?

   (a)   $4 + \square = 18$       (b)  $4 \times \square = 12$       (c)  $\square - 4 = 12$

   (d)   $\square + 8 = 8$       (e)  $8 \div 4 = \square$       (f)  $8 \div \square = 4$

3. Which of > or < goes in the gaps?

   (a)   25 . . . 26         (b)  11 . . . 4         (c)  100 . . . 99

4. (a) $7 + 3 = 10$  Which other 1-digit numbers add to 10?

   (b) $7 - 5 = 2$  Which other 1-digit numbers subtract to 2?

5. (a) Write down all the even numbers between 31 and 43.

   (b) Write down all the odd numbers that are less than 16.

   (c)

   | 5 | 14 | 25 | 30 | 37 | 38 | 45 |
   |---|----|----|----|----|----|----|

   Which number in this box is not divisible by either 2, 5 or 10?

6. Jamie bought 2 books and 5 magazines at this sale.

   What change did Jamie get from £5?

   SALE

   Books       £1·49
   Magazines      35p

7. What is the next statement in this number pattern?

$$2 + 10 = 12$$
$$12 + 10 = 22$$
$$22 + 10 = 32$$
$$32 + 10 = 42$$

8. On February 12th, these maximum temperatures (in°C) were recorded.

   | Amsterdam | 7 | Budapest | 8 | London | 10 |
   |-----------|----|----------|----|-------------|----|
   | Athens | 13 | Cairo | 12 | Los Angeles | 21 |
   | Bahrain | 18 | Dublin | 9 | Manila | 32 |
   | Bangkok | 33 | Geneva | 5 | Mecca | 24 |
   | Barbados | 29 | Honolulu | 27 | New Delhi | 19 |
   | Brussels | 6 | Libson | 15 | Paris | 11 |

   Geneva, Brussels, . . .
   Complete this list, writing the cities in order from coldest to warmest.

9. What is the place value of the 6 in these?

   (a) 63        (b) 4601        (c) 6410        (d) 406        (e) 6

10. Zeke has £1·95.

How many 18p chocolate bars can he buy?

11. What is the next number in these number patterns?

(a)  3, 2, 1, 3, 2, 1, 3, . . .         (b)  10, 30, 50, 70, . . .

12. Ann's birthday is July 3rd.
Jared's birthday is July 19th.

This year, Ann's birthday is on a Sunday.

What day of the week is Jared's birthday on this year?

13. (a)  What is the largest number that can be made using all of the digits 3, 6 and 5?

(b)  What is the smallest even number that can be made using two of the digits 3, 6 and 5?

14. There are 24 students in Raisa's maths. class.
One half of these students walk to school. One quarter of them wear glasses.

(a)  How many walk to school?

(b)  How many wear glasses?

15. In Cornwall there are 254 primary schools and 33 secondary schools.

(a)  How many more primary schools than secondary schools are there?

(b)  To the nearest 10, how many secondary schools are there?

(c)  To the nearest 100, how many primary schools are there?

16. Buns come in packets of 6.

    (a) How many packets are needed for 33 people?

    (b) How many buns are left over?

17. What is the next shape in this pattern?

18. Copy and complete.

    (a)  $31 + 16 = 30 + 1 + 10 + 6$
    $= 30 + \ldots + 1 + 6$
    $= \ldots + 7$
    $= \ldots$

    (b)  $32 + 49 = 32 + 50 - \ldots$
    $= 82 - \ldots$
    $= \ldots$

19. Copy this diagram.

    Put the numbers 6, 7, 12, 35, 56, 63, 77, 78 in the eight empty boxes so that the numbers on each side of the triangle add to 152.

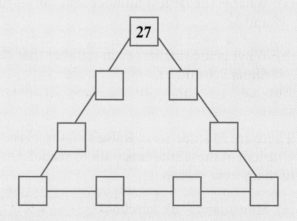

20. Nyasha was saving for a jacket which cost £29.
    She had saved £25.
    She did a calculation on her calculator and got – 4.

    (a) What calculation did Nyasha do?

    (b) Explain what – 4 means.

21. Find the missing number.

    (a)  2, 4, 6, . . . , 10        (b)  3, 6, 12, . . . , 48        (c)  16, . . . , 4, 2, 1

22. Five black and five red beads are threaded onto nylon thread as shown.

    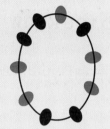

    (a) Show two other ways of threading these beads if no more than 2 beads of one colour are to be next to one another.

    (b) Find ways of threading these beads if the pattern of red and black beads must repeat.

23.  ● stands for a 1-digit number.

    What numbers might fit into  ■ + ■ = ● ? Is there more than one possible answer?

24. Debbie has one 50p coin, four 20p coins, two 10p coins and three 5p coins.

    Debbie buys a pen which costs 65p.
    She can pay for this with her 50p coin, one of her 10p coins and one of her 5p coins.

    What other coins could Debbie have used?

**DID YOU KNOW** that very important information in a problem can be easily missed?

Sometimes this is because we don't read the whole problem carefully enough before we begin to answer it.

Sometimes we read more meaning into a word, or sentence, than we should. That is, we make assumptions.

## DISCUSSION EXERCISE 1:1

• Read the nine instructions:

1. Pick up a pencil.
2. Write down the number 35.
3. Cross out the 3.
4. Double the 5.
5. Add on 10.
6. Take away 2.
7. Take away 10.
8. Add on 1.
9. Put your pencil down.

Do the first two instructions only.

What number did you finish with? **Discuss** with your group or class.

• As I was going to St. Ives,
I met a man with seven wives.
Every wife had seven sacks.
Every sack had seven cats.
Every cat had seven kittens.
How many were going to St. Ives?

**Discuss.**

- Find the answer to these problems.
  What assumptions might people make which would make it difficult to find the answers? **Discuss.**

  1. On Saturday, when it rained, Mr Brown's clothing got soaked. Even though he didn't have his head covered, not a hair on his head got wet. How could this be so?

  2. Garth was watching TV in bed. When the programme finished he used his remote control to turn the TV off. Then he got out of bed, went to the light switch at the other side of the room and turned the light off. He then walked back to his bed, a distance of 3 metres. Garth managed to get from the light switch to his bed before his bedroom was dark. How could this be so?

  3. A sick woman was in bed. In the room with her were her sister, a nurse and a doctor. A policeman, in the next room, heard the woman cry out "Help — he's going to shoot me." A shot was then heard. The policeman rushed into the room and arrested the nurse.

     How did the policeman know who to arrest?

- Think of some other problems, or riddles, which can be difficult to answer because of assumptions we make.
  **Discuss** these with your group or class.

## STEPS in PROBLEM SOLVING

The following steps can be used when solving a problem.

*Step 1*  Read the problem carefully.

*Step 2*  Write down the question you have to answer.
If necessary, rewrite the question in your own words.

*Step 3*  Write down the important information that is given.
If necessary, reorganise this information.

*Step 4*  Solve the problem. That is, answer the question.
You may have to decide whether to use $+, -, \times$ or $\div$.

## DISCUSSION EXERCISE 1:2

| times | take away | sum | difference | increase |
|-------|-----------|-----|------------|----------|

Which of +, −, ×, ÷ is suggested by the words in the box?

**Discuss** with your group or class.

Think of other words that mean add.
Think of other words that mean subtract.
Think of other words that mean multiply.
Think of other words that mean divide.

**Discuss** with your group or class.

- Subtract 17 from 25.

  How else might this instruction be worded? **Discuss.**

- Multiply 7 and 2.

  How else might this instruction be worded? **Discuss.**

- 12 apples were shared equally between 4 students. How many did each get?

  Do you need to +, −, × or ÷ to find the answer to this problem? **Discuss.**

- The school roll fell from 800 to 600. By how many did the roll fall?

  Do you need to +, −, × or ÷ to find the answer to this problem? **Discuss.**

- Make up some problems.
  Make sure you have some which need +, some which need −, some which need × and some which need ÷.

**Discuss** your problems with your group or class.

**Worked Example**    In 1991, there were 89 scouts in the Wayfield scout group. This number increased in 1992 by 4.

How many scouts were in the Wayfield scout group in 1992?

**Answer**    *The question is* "how many scouts were in the Wayfield scout group in 1992?"

*The important information is* "89"
                                                    "increased by 4"

*This information can be reorganised as* "add 4 to 89"

*The solution is* "89 + 4 = 93"

There were 93 scouts in 1992.

**Worked Example**    At a "Bring and Buy" stall, the cakes sold for £27·50, the sweets sold for £16, the vegetables sold for twice as much as the sweets and the crafts sold for three times as much as the sweets.

How much money was made at this stall?

**Answer**    *The question is* "how much money was made at this stall?"

*The question rewritten is* "how much did everything sell for?"

*The important information is* "cakes    £27·50
                                        sweets    £16·00
                                        vegetables-twice the sweets
                                        crafts-three times the sweets"

*This information can be reorganised as*    "cakes            £27·50
                                                            sweets            £16·00
                                                            vegetables      £32·00
                                                            crafts              £48·00"

*The solution is*  "£27·50 + £16·00 + £32·00 + £48·00 = £123·50"

£123·50 was made at this stall.

*Worked Example*    In an election for the captain of the netball club, Beatrice got 42 of the votes, Julia got 55 and Linda got the rest.

If 150 members of the netball club voted, who won the election?

*Answer*    *The question is* "who won the election?"

*The question rewritten is* "who got the most votes?"

*The important information is* "Beatrice 42 votes
Julia 55 votes
Linda the rest
150 voted"

*This information can be reorganised as* "Beatrice 42
Julia 55
Linda 150 − 55 − 42 = 53"

*The solution is* "Julia got the most votes."

Julia won the election.

---

## EXERCISE 1:3

1.  Of the £60 that Tony earned in the holidays, he saved £20. He spent £18 on a jacket, £11 on tapes and £4 on magazines.

    How much did Tony have left to spend?

2.  A cricket club has 184 members. 86 are good batters only, 45 are good at both batting and bowling. The rest are good bowlers only.

    How many are better batters than bowlers?

3.  Of the 300 people who voted for the new social club president, one-third of them voted for T. Allan. F. Patel got 98 votes and V. McBride got the rest.

    Who became the new president of the social club?

4.

| Wayside High School | | |
|---|---|---|
| | **roll last year** | **roll this year** |
| **Year 7** | 98 | 101 |
| **Year 8** | 79 | 98 |
| **Year 9** | 68 | 78 |
| **Year 10** | 75 | 70 |
| **Year 11** | 44 | 48 |
| **Year 12** | 37 | 39 |

Did the total school roll increase or decrease this year? By how much did it increase or decrease?

5. Brent and Grant walked 1500 metres along a beach.
Brent's steps were 10cm longer than Grant's.

How many steps did Grant take if each of Brent's steps was 60cm long?

6. Yesterday, in a sale, a shop sold twice as many cricket bats as tennis racquets. They sold 15 fewer tennis racquets than footballs.

If this shop sold 20 footballs, how many cricket bats were sold?

Review 1    Last year there were 124 adult members and 65 junior members in the Broomfield Golf Club. This year there were 200 members which included 126 adults.

How many more junior members were there this year?

Review 2    For a barbecue, Elina decided to have sausages, chops and steaks.
She bought five times as many sausages as steaks and twice as many chops as steaks.

If Elina bought 8 chops, how many sausages, chops and steaks did she buy altogether?

# TOO MUCH or NOT ENOUGH INFORMATION

If we are not given enough information, we cannot solve a problem.
If we are given too much information, we must choose the information we need.

## DISCUSSION EXERCISE 1:4

- Deborah buys a hamburger.
  She gets 85p change.
  How much did the hamburger cost?

  Can you solve this problem? **Discuss.**

- James works in a supermarket after school.
  He earns £20 a week.
  He saves £10 a week.
  How many weeks will it take James to save £60 for the deposit on a set of drums worth £200?

  Is there information given in this problem that you will not use? **Discuss.**

- In a boutique sale, the dresses are on 3 racks.
  One rack has dresses priced at £19·50, on another the dresses are £29·50 and on the third rack they are £35.
  Shadia buys a dress in this sale. How much change does she get from £40?

  Are you given too little or too much information to solve this problem?
  **Discuss.**

## EXERCISE 1:5

**Read these problems carefully.**
**Which problems have too much information? Which have not enough information?**

**If it is possible to do so, find the answers.**

1.  200 tickets were sold for the school play. Adults paid £3 and children paid £1.

    How much were these 200 tickets sold for?

2. Anna threw three darts.
   One landed on the 19, another landed on the 3.

   Where did Anna's third dart land?

3. A total of 500 people went to a concert.
   220 women and 200 men went, making a total of 420 adults. The rest were children.
   Each adult paid £5 and each child paid £3.

   How much did these 500 people pay altogether?

4. Harry and Jacob both gained 3kg last year.
   At the beginning of the year, Harry weighed 47kg and Jacob weighed 41kg.

   How much did Jacob weigh at the end of the year?

5. Ben made some muffins. For each cup of flour or bran or oatmeal he used one egg.
   Ben made enough mixture to fill two trays completely and half fill a third tray.

   If each tray held 6 muffins, how many did Ben make?

6. In a maths. quiz there were 20 questions.
   Each student began with 20 points.
   Two points were added for each correct answer, one point was taken away for each incorrect answer and no point was gained or lost for a question not answered.
   In this quiz, Sally answered 6 questions correctly and 3 questions incorrectly.
   Megan answered only 5 questions.

   Who got more points, Megan or Sally?

7. William's house number has two digits.
   The sum of these digits is 10.

   What is William's house number?

8.  Kate has a number of pets.
    She has some white rabbits, some budgies and 3 cats.
    Kate has four times as many rabbits as cats and two more budgies than cats.

    How many of Kate's pets have wings?

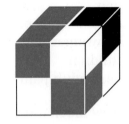

Review 1    Eight small cubes are glued together, as
            shown, to make one large cube.
            Of these small cubes, 3 are painted red.

            How many are painted black?

Review 2    Amy saved £10 to spend at the book sale.
            She bought two books for £3·50 each and three for 99p each.

            How much did Amy spend at the sale?

---

## PUZZLES 1:6

? ? ? ? ? ? ? ? ? ? ? ? ? ? ? ? ? ? ? ? ? ? ? ? ? ? ? ? ? ? ? ? ? ? ? ? ? ? ? ? ? ?

1.  James, Joe and John work in an office.
    One is the office manager, one is the sales manager and one is the
    personnel manager.
    Joe's wife is John's sister.
    The sales manager, who is an only child, earns the least.
    Joe earns more than the office manager.

    Which of these men does which job?

2.  Sandra, Sarah, Sheena and Sophie all read books in the summer
    holidays.
    Sandra read twice as many as Sarah.
    Sophie read five more than Sheena but six less than Sandra.
    Sheena read five books.

    How many did Sarah read?

? ? ? ? ? ? ? ? ? ? ? ? ? ? ? ? ? ? ? ? ? ? ? ? ? ? ? ? ? ? ? ? ? ? ? ? ? ? ? ? ? ?

## PRACTICAL EXERCISE 1:7

Make up a puzzle, similar to one of those on the previous page.

You may like to begin with the answer, then write facts to fit with this answer.

Test your puzzle on your group or another group.

---

### JUST FOR FUN

A crafty rich man suggested the following to a greedy rich man.

The crafty rich man said "Every day for 30 days I will give you £100,000. In return, on the first day you must give me 1 penny, on the second day 2 pennies, on the third day 4 pennies, on the fourth day 8 pennies, on the fifth day 16 pennies and so on. Each day, for the 30 days you must give me double what you gave me the day before."

The greedy rich man thought the crafty rich man was a fool. Was he a fool?

**DID YOU KNOW** that number names are often more useful than word names?

## DISCUSSION EXERCISE 2:1

- James goes on the number 216 bus to school. Today James noticed that the driver was wearing a badge with the number 245.

  Think of all the number names that are used in transport. **Discuss** with your group or class.

- Alma's family were abroad for a holiday. Alma told her sister to meet her on the corner of 59th Street and 3rd Avenue.

  Which country do you think Alma's family went to?

  Do you think it is a good idea for city streets to have number names instead of word names? **Discuss** with your neighbour or group.

- Choose a sport such as football, sailing etc.

  **Discuss** the number names that are used in this sport.


- Choose a job such as nursing, farming etc.

  **Discuss** the number names that are used in this job.


- What number names are used in your school? **Discuss.**


-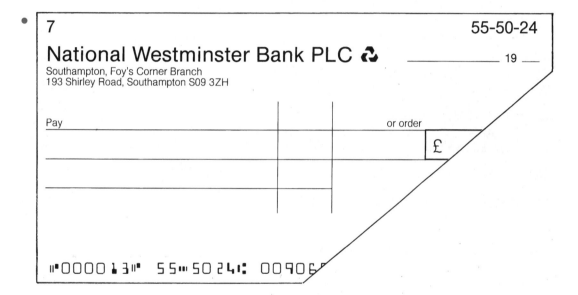

One of the number names that banks use is the number that gives the name of the bank.

What other number names do banks use? **Discuss** with your group.

- Adele's family went to Switzerland for a skiing holiday. Each time Adele saw, or heard, a number name she made a note of it. Adele used these notes when she wrote a report for her maths. class.

  What might Adele have written in her report? **Discuss.**

  You might like to write Adele's report for her.

## PLACE VALUE

The number 9674108 is shown below, written on a **place value chart**.

| Millions | Hundreds of Thousands | Tens of Thousands | Thousands | Hundreds | Tens | Units (ones) |
|---|---|---|---|---|---|---|
| 9 | 6 | 7 | 4 | 1 | 0 | 8 |

*Worked Example*    What is the place value of the 7 in these?    (a) 675
(b) 870031

*Answer*    (a) In 675, the 7 is in the tens place. We say that the place value of the 7 is tens.

(b) In 870031, the 7 is in the tens of thousands place. We say that the place value of the 7 is tens of thousands.

Large numbers are read in groups of three.

| MILLIONS | | | THOUSANDS | | | | | |
|---|---|---|---|---|---|---|---|---|
| Hundreds | Tens | Units | Hundreds | Tens | Units | Hundreds | Tens | Units |
|  |  | 9 | 6 | 7 | 4 | 1 | 0 | 8 |

The number 9674108 is read as "nine million, six hundred and seventy four thousand, one hundred and eight".

The number system we use is a **decimal system**. The place value of each number is ten times as large as the place value of the number immediately to the right.

*Worked Example*    How many times larger is the 9 in 39450 than in 897?

*Answer*

| Tens of Thousands | Thousands | Hundreds | Tens | Units |
|---|---|---|---|---|
| 3 | 9 | 4 | 5 | 0 |
|  |  | 8 | 9 | 7 |

The 9 in 39450 is two places to the left of the 9 in 897.
The 9 in 39450 is 10 × 10 times as large as the 9 in 897.
That is, the 9 in 39450 is 100 times as large as the 9 in 897.

30

## DISCUSSION EXERCISE 2:2

● A day coach trip to the Blackpool Illuminations costs £38.
The 100 people who went on this coach trip paid a total of £3800.

A carvery meal at the Hilltop Hotel costs £13.
A group of 10 people paid a total of £130.

Booklets are stacked in piles of 100. Each booklet is 2mm thick.
The height of each pile is 200mm.

**Discuss** how the £3800, £130 and 200mm can be found using a place value table.

● 460 ÷ 10        460 × 10        2300 × 100        2300 ÷ 100

How can place value be used to find the answer to these? **Discuss.**

## EXERCISE 2:3

1. Write these in words.

   (a) 306          (b) 7521          (c) 43978          (d) 12045

   (e) 662907       (f) 250018        (g) 12650          (h) 34800

   (i) 1590307      (j) 25482134      (k) 5062011        (l) 923010520

   (m) 744300042

2. What is the place value of the 8 in these?

   (a) 34859        (b) 584392        (c) 123468         (d) 4348213

   (e) 38050712     (f) 1800904       (g) 7342814        (h) 81234620

   (i) 5263087

3. Which digit in each of the numbers in **question 2** has place value of tens of thousands?

4. Copy the crossnumber and fill it in.
   **1.** across is done for you.

### Across

1. ten thousand, nine hundred and sixty four
4. one hundred and forty one
7. eighty
9. seventy six
10. nine thousand, two hundred
11. one thousand, five hundred and forty two
13. four hundred and twenty one
16. two thousand and three
18. eight thousand, four hundred and fifty three
21. six hundred
22. twenty two
24. sixty
25. twenty thousand and four hundred
27. seventy six
29. ninety thousand and forty five

### Down

1. one hundred and fifty nine
2. nine hundred and eighty thousand, four hundred and five
3. six thousand and two
5. four hundred and seventy four
6. one hundred and sixty two
8. eleven
12. fifty two thousand and sixty six
14. twelve
15. sixty eight
17. thirty thousand and seventy four
19. four hundred
20. three hundred and twenty
23. two hundred and nine
25. twenty nine
26. forty
28. sixty five

5. Which number is (a) ten times as large as 82

    (b) one hundred times as large as 17

    (c) ten times as large as 423

    (d) one hundred times as large as 321

    (e) ten times as large as 2463

    (f) ten times as large as 7

    (g) one hundred times as large as 4

    (h) ten times smaller than 8000

    (i) one hundred times smaller than 8000?

6. Use place value to find the answer to these.

    2400    26100

    (a) 24 × 100      (b) 261 × 100      (c) 9 × 10

    (d) 11 × 10       (e) 260 ÷ 10       (f) 2000 ÷ 10

    (g) 12000 ÷ 100   (h) 3500 ÷ 100

7. Pinocchio was written in the 19th century. The sum of the digits of the year in which it was written is 20. The difference between the tens digit and the thousands digit is 7.

    In which year was Pinocchio written?

**Review 1**   Write these in figures.

    (a) two thousand and ten

    (b) five hundred and forty nine thousand, two hundred and one

    (c) thirty five million, seven hundred and two thousand, one hundred and twenty

**Review 2**  Write these in words.

(a) 25415  (b) 35400830  (c) 1090425

**Review 3**  (a) Which number is ten times as large as 824?

(b) Which number is one hundred times as large as 29?

(c) Which number is one hundred times smaller than 500?

(d) Which number is ten times smaller than 500?

**Review 4**  Use place value to find the answer to these.

(a) $82 \times 100$  (b) $20 \times 100$  (c) $20 \div 10$

(d) $450 \div 10$  (e) $54000 \div 100$  (f) $250 \times 10$

## PUZZLE 2:4

??????????????????????????????????????????????
```
        S T A N D        2 3 1 8 5
        D E N S E        1 8 3 2 4
        N A S T Y        7 3 2 4 5
        T A S T E        4 6 2 1 6
        H A N D Y        8 3 1 8 6
```

Simon got these five words and their codes mixed up. Shardia sorted them out.
Which code did Shardia put beside each word?
??????????????????????????????????????????????

# INVESTIGATION 2:5

## CONSECUTIVE DIGITS

Digits are consecutive if they follow one another.
For instance, 4 and 5 are consecutive as are 3 and 2.
The digits 6 and 8 are not consecutive since the digit 7 comes between them.

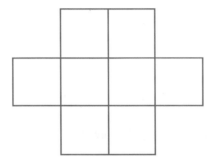

**Investigate** how to place the digits 1, 2, 3, 4, 5, 6, 7 and 8 in these boxes so that no two boxes with a common side have consecutive digits.

**What if** the boxes with consecutive digits may not have any part in common, not even a corner?

**What if** eight other digits were chosen?

**What if** the eight boxes were arranged as shown below?

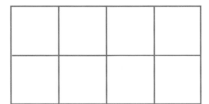

**What if** the eight boxes were arranged in some other way?

## ORDERING WHOLE NUMBERS

| DISCUSSION EXERCISE 2:6 |
|---|

- Anna 78   Huda 83   Colin 69   Sara 82   Chung 72   Nicola 75   James 64

  Seven students got these marks in a test.

  Who was top? Who was third? How many were below Nicola? **Discuss.**

- At Noah's Takeaway, consecutive numbers are given to customers as they order their meals.

**Rebecca    Adam    Ali    Alison    Melissa    Joan    Andrew**

Did Alison order before Rebecca?
How many of the people shown ordered after Joan?
Who ordered first? Who ordered last?
In which order were these people served? **Discuss.**

- A.D. 3459   H.A. 1258   B.D. 16724   C.T. 3541   M.M. 425
  A.Z. 7815   T.B. 2301   T.N. 895     D.E. 3424   B.O. 5213
  N.F. 841    F.T. 12354  P.D. 1999    D.Y. 13041  K.N. 6234
  T.M. 7782   O.U. 441    S.A. 982

  As each person arrived for a scout jamboree they were given a number.

  Which of the above scouts arrived first?
  In which order did they arrive? **Discuss.**

- **Discuss** other examples where numbers would be put in order. In which of these would the numbers be written in order from smallest to largest? In which would they be written from largest to smallest?

- **Discuss** how to write the following numbers in order.

  | 1249 | 4291 | 241   | 32914 | 4192 | 1924 |
  |------|------|-------|-------|------|------|
  | 149  | 2149 | 32941 | 4912  | 1942 |      |

- Write down any 20 numbers. Have other students in your group write these numbers in order.

---

## GAME 2:7

---

**LADDERS: a game for a group.**

Choose a leader.
The other students each draw a "ladder" like that shown.

The leader chooses ten numbers between 0 and 20 and calls these one at a time.
As the leader calls each number, the students put it on their ladders. The numbers must be put in order. For instance, suppose the number 17 is called after a student has put the numbers 15 and 18 on the top two rungs of the ladder. The number 17 cannot be put on this student's ladder.

The winner is the student who is able to put more numbers than anyone else on his or her ladder.
The winner becomes the leader for the next round.

**Variation** The leader may choose to call ten numbers from 0 to 50 or from 100 to 120 or from 1000 to 1030 etc.

## EXERCISE 2:8

1.

| 326 | 3147 | 5435 |
|---|---|---|
| 362 | 149003 | 3174 |
| 194301 | 96825 | 33033 |
| 42008 | 5534 | 98625 |
| 10001 | 24800 | 491054 |
| 3552220 | 3552022 | 3552202 |
| 9999 | 3333 | 491045 |

Copy the diagram.

Choose the larger of each of the following pairs of numbers. Shade the part of the diagram that has this number.

For instance, 362 is larger than 326 so the part of the diagram which has 362 is shaded.

| | | |
|---|---|---|
| 326, 362 | 5534, 5435 | 42008, 24800 |
| 33033, 3333 | 96825, 98625 | 149003, 194301 |
| 491054, 491045 | 9999, 10001 | 3147, 3174 |
| 3552220, 3552022 | 3552022, 3552202 | |

What pattern do the shaded parts make?

2. Write down the number that is ten more than

   (a) 7823    (b) 1259    (c) 368093    (d) 1234908    (e) 2783998.

3. Write down the number that is one hundred less than each of the numbers in **question 2.**

4. What is the smallest number that can be made

   (a) using all of the digits 7, 2, 3, 4

   (b) using two of the digits 3, 9, 5, 4

   (c) using three different odd digits?

5. Which of these statements are true?

   (a) 298 < 289   (b) 5369 > 5396   (c) 9998 < 10101   (d) 1134134 > 1131434

6. 

| A.H. 178 | B.D. 203 | C.F. 194 | A.D. 210 | E.M. 187 | H.M. 192 |
|----------|----------|----------|----------|----------|----------|
| D.B. 159 | A.T. 168 | I.N. 162 | B.Y. 163 | W.A. 175 | T.D. 201 |
| M.N. 190 | N.M. 181 | P.F. 200 | J.B. 189 | B.A. 154 | B.E. 169 |

   This list shows the time (in seconds) some students took to run around their school buildings.

   (a) Who ran the fastest?

   (b) Who finished last?

   (c) In which order did these students finish?

7. 

| | Berlin | Bombay | Cape Town | Darwin | London | Mexico City | Moscow | New York | Paris | Peking | Rome | Tokyo |
|---|---|---|---|---|---|---|---|---|---|---|---|---|
| Berlin | | 6290 | 9620 | 12930 | 920 | 9720 | 1600 | 6370 | 870 | 7350 | 1180 | 8910 |
| Bombay | 6290 | | 8260 | 7250 | 7180 | 15650 | 5040 | 12540 | 7020 | 4770 | 6190 | 6740 |
| Cape Town | 9620 | 8260 | | 11180 | 9660 | 13700 | 10130 | 12550 | 9400 | 12950 | 8450 | 14600 |
| Darwin | 12930 | 7250 | 11180 | | 13840 | 14610 | 11340 | 16030 | 13800 | 6000 | 13180 | 5420 |
| London | 920 | 7180 | 9660 | 13840 | | 8920 | 2490 | 5570 | 340 | 8130 | 1430 | 9550 |
| Mexico City | 9720 | 15650 | 13700 | 14610 | 8920 | | 10760 | 3360 | 9180 | 12450 | 10230 | 11320 |
| Moscow | 1600 | 5040 | 10130 | 11340 | 2490 | 10760 | | 7500 | 2480 | 5790 | 2370 | 7480 |
| New York | 6370 | 12540 | 12550 | 16030 | 5570 | 3360 | 7500 | | 5830 | 10980 | 6880 | 10830 |
| Paris | 870 | 7020 | 9400 | 13800 | 340 | 9180 | 2480 | 5830 | | 8210 | 1100 | 9700 |
| Peking | 7350 | 4770 | 12950 | 6000 | 8130 | 12450 | 5790 | 10980 | 8210 | | 8120 | 2100 |
| Rome | 1180 | 6190 | 8450 | 13180 | 1430 | 10230 | 2370 | 6880 | 1100 | 8120 | | 9850 |
| Tokyo | 8910 | 6740 | 14600 | 5420 | 9550 | 11320 | 7480 | 10830 | 9700 | 2100 | 9850 | |

   This chart gives the distances (to the nearest ten kilometres) between some of the cities in the world.

   (a) What is the greatest distance between any two of the cities on the chart? Between which two cities is this?

   (b) Which of the cities is the greatest distance from Cape Town?

   (c) Which of the cities is closest to Moscow?

8. Write the numbers in these lists in order, from the smallest to the largest.

   (a) 3041, 3401, 3104, 3410

   (b) 1431, 1354, 1541, 1435, 1543

   (c) 82345, 82352, 82435, 82325

   (d) 614248, 624149, 614420, 621447

**Review 1** Which of these statements are true?

   (a) 787 < 878

   (b) 112013 > 99999

   (c) 386245 < 368254

**Review 2** Write these numbers in order, from the smallest to the largest.

   86457    78654    87645    78546    87465    78645    86745

**Review 3**

**10.4 Recruitment of UK Service personnel to each Service**                                                                                                                          Number

|  | 1978/79 | 1979/80 | 1980/81 | 1981/82 | 1982/83 | 1983/84 | 1984/85 | 1985/86 | 1986/87 | 1987/88 | 1988/89 |
|---|---|---|---|---|---|---|---|---|---|---|---|
| **All services:** | | | | | | | | | | | |
| Male | 38 774 | 46 206 | 46 693 | 21 188 | 19 342 | 33 760 | 32 076 | 30 407 | 31 147 | 31 215 | 30 862 |
| Female | 4 592 | 4 446 | 3 795 | 1 419 | 2 305 | 3 231 | 2 645 | 2 244 | 2 902 | 2 611 | 3 001 |
| Total | 43 366 | 50 652 | 50 488 | 22 607 | 21 647 | 36 991 | 34 721 | 32 651 | 34 049 | 33 826 | 33 863 |
| **Royal Navy:** | | | | | | | | | | | |
| Male | 5 978 | 7 701 | 8 130 | 3 353 | 3 078 | 4 223 | 4 231 | 3 987 | 4 791 | 4 601 | 4 598 |
| Female | 813 | 825 | 958 | 452 | 506 | 562 | 351 | 289 | 545 | 580 | 700 |
| Total | 6 791 | 8 526 | 9 088 | 3 805 | 3 584 | 4 785 | 4 582 | 4 276 | 5 336 | 5 181 | 5 298 |
| **Royal Marines:** | | | | | | | | | | | |
| Male | 1 282 | 1 676 | 1 674 | 699 | 447 | 447 | 954 | 1 093 | 1 233 | 991 | 937 |
| Total | 1 282 | 1 676 | 1 674 | 699 | 447 | 447 | 954 | 1 093 | 1 233 | 991 | 937 |
| **Army:** | | | | | | | | | | | |
| Male | 23 528 | 27 164 | 27 241 | 13 603 | 11 679 | 20 811 | 20 914 | 19 173 | 18 718 | 19 895 | 19 921 |
| Female | 1 726 | 2 025 | 1 630 | 601 | 1 392 | 1 537 | 1 364 | 1 095 | 1 200 | 1 146 | 1 427 |
| Total | 25 254 | 29 189 | 28 871 | 14 204 | 13 071 | 22 348 | 22 278 | 20 268 | 19 918 | 21 041 | 21 348 |
| **Royal Air Force:** | | | | | | | | | | | |
| Male | 7 986 | 9 665 | 9 648 | 3 533 | 4 138 | 8 279 | 5 977 | 6 154 | 6 405 | 5 728 | 5 406 |
| Female | 2 053 | 1 596 | 1 207 | 366 | 407 | 1 132 | 930 | 860 | 1 157 | 885 | 874 |
| Total | 10 039 | 11 261 | 10 855 | 3 899 | 4 545 | 9 411 | 6 907 | 7 014 | 7 562 | 6 613 | 6 280 |

*Source Ministry of Defence*

**Source: Key Data 1990/91**

(a) In which year was the smallest number of females recruited to the Royal Navy?

(b) In which year was the greatest number of people recruited to all services?

(c) In which year, and to which service, was the greatest number of males recruited?

## INVESTIGATION 2:9

### NUMBERS from DIGITS

How many 3-digit numbers can be made from the digits 2, 5, 4, 7, 3 if all three digits must be different? Investigate.

What if the digits were 2, 5, 0, 7, 3?

What if all three digits did not have to be different?

What if there were only four digits to choose from?

What if ...

## GAME 2:10

### YES/NO: a game for a group.

Choose a leader.
The leader writes down a number, without showing it to anyone.

The rest of the students in the group have to find this number.
They do this by taking turns to ask the leader questions.
The leader may only answer Yes or No to each question.

The student who is able to correctly name the number is the leader for the next round.

Some of the questions that might be asked are:
"Is the number greater than 100?"
"Is the number even?"
"Does it have two digits?"
"Is the number between 40 and 70?"

## PRACTICAL EXERCISE 2:11

Collect pictures, which include numbers, from newspapers, magazines and brochures.

Use these to make an interesting poster or collage or mural which has a theme or tells a story.

## PUZZLE 2:12

I am a number between one and ten.

My first is in ten but not in three.
My second is in five but not in four.
My third is in one but not in five.
My last is in three but not in two.

What number am I?

## JUST FOR FUN

Codes may be written by giving each letter of the alphabet a number.

| A simple code is: | A | B | C | D | E | F | G | H | I | J | ... |
|---|---|---|---|---|---|---|---|---|---|---|---|
| | 1 | 2 | 3 | 4 | 5 | 6 | 7 | 8 | 9 | 10 | ... |
| Another code is: | A | B | C | D | E | F | G | H | I | J | ... |
| | 2 | 3 | 4 | 5 | 6 | 7 | 8 | 9 | 10 | 11 | ... |
| Another code is: | A | B | C | D | E | F | G | H | I | J | ... |
| | 2 | 1 | 4 | 3 | 6 | 5 | 8 | 7 | 10 | 9 | ... |

Write a sentence.
Code this sentence using one of the above codes or a code of your own.

Have other members of your group, or your neighbour, try to "crack your code".

# Calculation: mental methods

**DID YOU KNOW** that we can find the answer to multiplications such as 6 × 8 by using the multiplication facts of up to 5 × 5?

---

## DISCUSSION EXERCISE 3:1

---

**Discuss** the following method of finding the answer to 6 × 8.

*Step 1*    Subtract each of 6 and 8 from 10 to get 4 and 2.

*Step 2*    Multiply these two new numbers.
This gives the units digit.

*Step 3*    Write down the original numbers, one under the other as shown.
Write down the new numbers from step 1, one under the other as shown.
Subtract diagonally to get the tens digit.

|   |   |
|---|---|
| 6 | 4 |
| 8 | 2 |

*Step 4*    Write down the tens digit followed by the units digit to get the answer.

Does this method work for multiplying any two 1-digit numbers? **Discuss.**

## MULTIPLYING and DIVIDING mentally

We can use this table to find the answer
to any multiplication from
$1 \times 1$ to $10 \times 10$. Learn these.

We can also use this table to find the
answers to divisions such as $72 \div 9$.
Learn these.

| ×  | 1  | 2  | 3  | 4  | 5  | 6  | 7  | 8  | 9  | 10  |
|----|----|----|----|----|----|----|----|----|----|-----|
| 1  | 1  | 2  | 3  | 4  | 5  | 6  | 7  | 8  | 9  | 10  |
| 2  | 2  | 4  | 6  | 8  | 10 | 12 | 14 | 16 | 18 | 20  |
| 3  | 3  | 6  | 9  | 12 | 15 | 18 | 21 | 24 | 27 | 30  |
| 4  | 4  | 8  | 12 | 16 | 20 | 24 | 28 | 32 | 36 | 40  |
| 5  | 5  | 10 | 15 | 20 | 25 | 30 | 35 | 40 | 45 | 50  |
| 6  | 6  | 12 | 18 | 24 | 30 | 36 | 42 | 48 | 54 | 60  |
| 7  | 7  | 14 | 21 | 28 | 35 | 42 | 49 | 56 | 63 | 70  |
| 8  | 8  | 16 | 24 | 32 | 40 | 48 | 56 | 64 | 72 | 80  |
| 9  | 9  | 18 | 27 | 36 | 45 | 54 | 63 | 72 | 81 | 90  |
| 10 | 10 | 20 | 30 | 40 | 50 | 60 | 70 | 80 | 90 | 100 |

A division such as $72 \div 9$ may also be written as $\frac{72}{9}$ .

## DISCUSSION and PRACTICAL EXERCISE 3:2

**Work in pairs.**

1.  Practise multiplying and dividing "in your head" in one or more of the
    following ways.

    - One student calls 20 multiplications ($6 \times 4, 7 \times 3$ etc.). The other student
      calls the answers (24, 21 etc.) and notes the time it took to get the correct
      answers. The students then swap roles.

    - One student calls multiplications for 2 minutes. The other student calls
      the answers and notes the number of correct answers given in this time.
      The students then swap roles.

    - Repeat one or both of the above, firstly with divisions and then with
      mixed multiplication and division.

2.  Discuss other ways of practising the multiplication and division facts.
    Use one of these to practise these facts.

*Worked Example*    Shona runs 4 km each morning.

(a) How far does she run in one week?

(b) How many days does it take Shona to run 36 km?

*Answer*    (a) Each week Shona runs $4 \times 7 = 28$ km.

(b) Number of days to run 36 km is $36 \div 4 = 9$ days.

## EXERCISE 3:3

1. Find the missing numbers.

   (a) $7 \times 6 = \square$      (b) $9 \times 2 = \square$      (c) $4 \times 6 = \square$      (d) $3 \times \square = 27$

   (e) $6 \times \square = 48$      (f) $5 \times \square = 30$      (g) $\square \times 8 = 40$      (h) $\square \times 9 = 72$

   (i) $12 \div 3 = \square$      (j) $49 \div 7 = \square$      (k) $\square \div 6 = 7$      (1) $81 \div \square = 9$

   (m) $\frac{24}{4} = \square$      (n) $\frac{56}{7} = \square$      (o) $\frac{\square}{3} = 3$      (p) $\frac{45}{\square} = 5$

2. Copy and complete these multiplication squares.

| × | 3 | 5 | 6 |
|---|---|---|---|
| 2 |   |   |   |
| 4 |   |   |   |
| 5 |   | 25 |   |

(a)

| × | 4 | 2 | 7 |
|---|---|---|---|
| 3 |   |   |   |
|   |   |   | 28 |
| 8 |   |   |   |

(b)

| × | 3 |   | 8 |
|---|---|---|---|
|   |   | 40 |   |
| 4 | 20 |   |   |
| 9 |   |   |   |

(c)

| × | 9 | 10 |   |
|---|---|----|---|
| 8 |   |   | 48 |
|   | 63 |   |   |
|   |   |   | 12 |

(d)

3. For each event that a school won, 3 points were given.
   Harrowdale School won 9 events.

   How many points did this school get?

4. A card of 24 tablets has 4 rows of tablets.

   How many tablets are there on each row?

5. Eggs are packed 6 to a box.

   How many eggs are in     (a) 10 boxes     (b) 8 boxes     (c) 5 boxes?

6. Fifty apricots are to be packed 8 to a tray.

   (a) How many trays can be completely filled?

   (b) How many apricots will be left over?

7. Garth made a tray of chocolate fudge. He cut it into 3 rows, each with 8 pieces.

   How many pieces of chocolate fudge did Garth get from this tray?

8. A class of 30 students is to be divided into groups.

   How can this be done if the groups are to be the same size?

9.

| 6 | × |   | = |   |
|---|---|---|---|---|
| ÷ | ■ | × | ■ | ÷ |
|   | ÷ | 1 | = | 3 |
| = | ■ | = | ■ | = |
|   | × | 5 | = |   |

Copy this diagram.

Fill in the blank squares with numbers so that all the calculations are correct.

**Review 1**    Find the answer to these.

     (a) $7 \times 8$    (b) $5 \times 3$    (c) $28 \div 4$    (d) $48 \div 6$    (e) $9 \times 10$

     (f) $9 \times 5$    (g) $18 \div 3$    (h) $\frac{18}{2}$    (i) $\frac{32}{8}$

**Review 2**    (a) How many days are there in 7 complete weeks?

             (b) How many complete weeks are there in 63 days?

---

## DISCUSSION EXERCISE 3:4

- $$\square \times \square = 18 \qquad 24 \div \square = \square$$

  Complete the multiplication and division in as many different ways as possible. **Discuss** with your neighbour or your group.

  Write a multiplication or division similar to those above. Give it to your neighbour, or group, to complete in as many different ways as possible.

- $$6 \times 7 = 42 \qquad 3 \times 5 = 15 \qquad 42 \div 7 = 6 \qquad 64 \div 8 = 8$$

  Make up a "story" for each of these calculations. **Discuss** your "stories" with your neighbour or group or class.

- **Discuss** ways of completing this multiplication square.

| × |   |    |
|---|---|----|
|   |   | 18 |
|   | 56 |   |

---

## GAME 3:5

---

**FIVE CARDS: a game for a group of up to 6 students.**

| | |
|---|---|
| **Equipment** | A pack of cards for each group. |
| **Rules** | The face cards (J, Q, K) all count as 10. Aces count as 1. |
| **The Play** | The dealer deals five cards to each student, then two cards face up on the table. The rest of the pack is placed face down. |
| | Students take turns to play either one card or two cards. One card may be played if it is the same as one of the cards on the table. Two cards may be played if the numbers on these cards either add to, or subtract to, or multiply to, or divide to, the same as one of the cards on the table. |

If a student is unable to play a card, a card must be picked up from the pack.

The first student to be left with no cards is the winner.

## ADDING and SUBTRACTING mentally

| INVESTIGATION 3:6 |
| --- |

---

### MAGIC SQUARES

1.  In a magic square the numbers on each row, each column and each diagonal add to the same total.

    The numbers 1, 2, 3, 4, 5, 6, 7, 8 and 9 are placed as shown to make a magic square.

| 2 | 9 | 4 |
|---|---|---|
| 7 | 5 | 3 |
| 6 | 1 | 8 |

**Investigate** other ways of placing these numbers to make magic squares.

2.  Can a magic square be made from the first 9 even numbers? **Investigate.**

    **What if** odd numbers were used instead of even numbers?

3.

   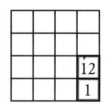

Each of the six small blocks is to be placed on the large grid to make a magic square.

**Investigate** ways of doing this if the  block is placed as shown.

**What if** the $\frac{12}{1}$ block was put somewhere else?

## INVESTIGATION 3:7

### POOL BALLS

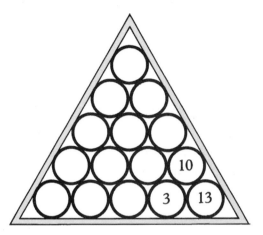

In the game of pool, 15 balls numbered 1 to 15 are used. At the beginning of a game, these balls are placed in a "triangle" as shown.

In one arrangement, the number on any ball is the same as the difference between the numbers on the two balls just below. If in this arrangement, the balls numbered 10, 3 and 13 are in the places shown, find the numbers on the other balls.

Is there more than one way of arranging the other balls? **Investigate.**

**What if** the 10, 3 and 13 did not need to be in the places shown?

Is it possible to arrange the balls so that the number on any ball is equal to the sum of the numbers on the two balls just below? **Investigate.**

**Investigate** number patterns that can be made with different arrangements of the balls. You could look at patterns made with the even and odd numbers, the sums of the numbers in all the small triangles within the large triangle, ...

## JUST FOR FUN

1.　　A B　　Replace A, B and C with numbers to make this addition
　　　+ C B　　correct.
　　　‾‾‾‾‾
　　　B B A

2. Make up some more additions in which the numbers are replaced by letters.

3.　　A B　　A could be 1, B could be 2 and C could be 4.
　　×　 B　　Could A, B, C have other values?
　　‾‾‾‾‾
　　　B C

4.　　A B　　What values might A, B and C have?
　　×　 C
　　‾‾‾‾‾
　　　C B

5. Make up some more multiplications in which the numbers are replaced by letters.

# Calculation: pencil and paper methods

**DID YOU KNOW** that one of the first number systems to be written down was the Egyptian system?

---

### DISCUSSION EXERCISE 4:1

---

The Egyptian number system had symbols for 1, 10, 100, 1000, 10000, 100000, 1000000.

The symbol for 1 was a stroke |

for 10 was a heel bone    ∩

for 100 was a coiled rope    ∂ or ⊚ or ℓ

for 1000 was a lotus flower    ⚇ or ⚇

for 10000 was a bent finger    ⌐ or ⌐

for 100000 was a tadpole    ⌐ or ⌐

for 1000000 was an excited man    ⚇ or ⚇ or ⚇

The order in which the symbols were written was not important.

For instance, 23 could be written as   ∩∩||| or |∩∩|| or ||∩ etc.
        ∩|

9 could be written as   ||||||   or   ||||   or   ||||||||| etc.
        |||        |||||

Write some numbers using the Egyptian system. Discuss with your group.

Would it be easy to multiply by 10 in this system? Discuss.

How could you add two numbers in this system? Discuss.

# ADDING and SUBTRACTING 3-digit NUMBERS:
## pencil and paper methods

## DISCUSSION EXERCISE 4:2

- Peta's method for adding and subtracting is shown below.

$$347 \quad 300 + 500 = 800 \qquad\qquad 800 + 100 = 900$$
$$+ 595 \qquad 40 + 90 = 130 = 100 + 30 \qquad 30 + 10 = 40$$
$$\overline{\phantom{xxxx}} \qquad\qquad 7 + 5 = 12 = 10 + 2 \qquad\qquad\qquad 2$$
$$\text{Answer} \; \overline{942}$$

$$854 \quad 800 - 200 = \boxed{600}$$
$$- 218 \qquad 50 - 10 = 40$$
$$\overline{\phantom{xxxx}} \qquad\qquad 4 \; 8$$
$$\boxed{30}$$
$$14 - 8 = \boxed{6}$$
$$636 \; \text{Answer}$$

**Discuss** Peta's methods.

- What other methods could you use to add and subtract? **Discuss.**

- Allan added 321 and 497. He got the answer 518.
  Felicity said that this couldn't be correct.
  How could Felicity tell? **Discuss.**

Always check that your answers are reasonable.
For instance, if we add 237 and 122 we must get an answer greater than 300.

# EXERCISE 4:3

1. Copy the diagrams.

   The number in any square is found by adding the numbers in the two circles on either side of the square.

   Find the missing numbers.

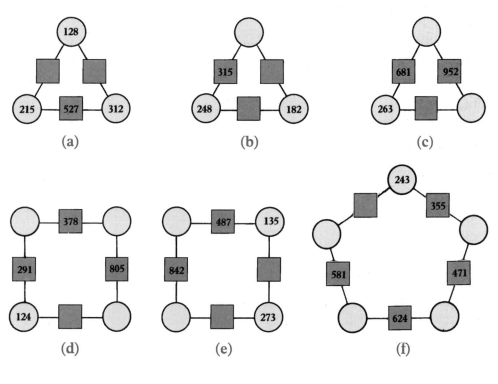

    (a)                   (b)                  (c)

    (d)                   (e)                  (f)

2. $\square + \square = 213$ $\qquad\qquad$ $\square - 123 = \square$

   Complete the above addition and subtraction in at least 10 different ways.

3. Use all the digits 8, 7, 6, 5, 4, 3 to make two 3-digit numbers so that

   (a) the sum of these two numbers is as large as possible

   (b) the sum is as small as possible

   (c) the difference between these two numbers is as small as possible.

   Is there more than one answer to each of these?

4. Michael has £452. Bryce has £254.

   How much more does Michael have?

5. A car dealer sold 249 cars in 1991. This was 38 more than in 1990.

   How many cars did this dealer sell in 1990?

6. Adam and Nema both collect stamps. Adam has 78 fewer than Nema.

   How many stamps does Nema have if Adam has 125?

7.
   This table shows the number of trays of peaches packed at two orchards in one week. The fruit was graded as either Export grade or Local Market grade.

| Day | Orchard A | | Orchard B | |
|-----|--------|-------|--------|-------|
|     | Export | Local | Export | Local |
| M   | 272    | 145   | 162    | 104   |
| Tu  | 268    | 151   | 205    | 82    |
| W   | 183    | 240   | 189    | 95    |
| Th  | 203    | 159   | 146    | 65    |
| F   | 142    | 97    | 82     | 54    |

   (a) How many trays of Export grade peaches did orchard B pack on Tuesday?

   (b) How many more trays of Export grade than Local Market grade did orchard B pack on Tuesday?

   (c) On which day did orchard A pack the most trays?

   (d) Which orchard packed more trays in the week? How many more?

Review 1   Two sisters each had a holiday job. Lydia earned £237 and Annabel earned £189. They added the money together to buy new furniture for their bedroom.

   How much money did they have altogether?

Review 2   A farmer had 256 sheep. She sold 137.

   How many sheep did this farmer have left?

## GAME 4:4

### THREE DIGITS

Draw this grid in your book. **h** is hundreds,
**t** is tens, **u** is units.

Choose a leader.

| **h** | **t** | **u** |
|---|---|---|
|  |  |  |
|  |  |  |

The leader chooses six different digits from 0 to 9. The leader calls these, one at a time.

As each digit is called the other students in the group write it in one of the six parts of their grids. Each digit must be written *before* the next digit is called.

Once all six digits have been called, the students add the two three-digit numbers they have written.

The student with the highest total becomes the leader for the next round.

## PRACTICAL EXERCISE 4:5

Make up a crossnumber. Give it to the rest of your group, or your class, to solve.

You could copy one of the following crossnumber grids or you could make up one of your own.

| Across | Down |
|---|---|
| 1. | 1. |
| 2. | 2. |
| 4. | 3. |
| 5. | 6. |
| 7. | 8. |
| 9. | 10. |
| 11. | 12. |
| 14. | 13. |
| 15. | |
| 16. | |

| Across | Down |
|--------|------|
| 2. | 1. |
| 4. | 2. |
| 6. | 3. |
| 7. | 4. |
| 9. | 5. |
| 11. | 8. |
| 12. | 9. |
| 14. | 10. |
|    | 11. |
|    | 13. |

## INVESTIGATION 4:6

### PALINDROMIC NUMBERS

A number such as 373, which reads the same from left to right as it does from right to left, is a palindromic number.
Other examples are 88 and 1441.

Many palindromic numbers can be made as follows.

| | |
|---|---|
| Begin with any number, say | 168 |
| Reverse the digits | 861 |
| Add | 1029 |
| Reverse the digits | 9201 |
| Add | 10230 |
| Reverse the digits | 03201 |
| Add | 13431 |

It took 3 reversals of the digits to make the palindromic number 13431.

Investigate the number of reversals needed to make palindromic numbers from other numbers.

Does there seem to be a connection between the sum of the digits of a number and the number of reversals needed to make a palindromic number? Investigate.

## MULTIPLYING and DIVIDING 2-digit NUMBERS by 1-digit NUMBERS: pencil and paper methods

---
**DISCUSSION EXERCISE 4:7**
---

- Two students multiplied 95 × 4 as follows.

Gina's method:  90 × 4 = 360
5 × 4 = 20
380 Answer

Aba's method: 95
× 4
2
380

Discuss these and other methods of multiplying.

- Gina and Aba did the division 95 ÷ 4 as follows.

Gina's method:

$$4 \overline{)95}$$
23
8    4 × 2 = 8
15
12    4 × 3 = 12
3

Answer 23 with remainder 3

Aba's method: 95
40    4 × 10
55
40    4 × 10
15
12    4 × 3
3    23

Answer 23 remainder 3

Discuss these and other methods of dividing.

---
**EXERCISE 4:8**
---

1. Do these multiplications.

(a) 35 × 7    (b) 49 × 5    (c) 73 × 6    (d) 82 × 4    (e) 68 × 8

(f) 28 × 9    (g) 43 × 3    (h) 37 × 2    (i) 74 × 7

2. Find the answer to these.

   (a) $69 \div 3$   (b) $99 \div 9$   (c) $78 \div 2$   (d) $90 \div 6$   (e) $96 \div 8$

   (f) $\frac{85}{5}$   (g) $\frac{55}{4}$   (h) $\frac{80}{3}$   (i) $\frac{94}{7}$

3. Find the remainder in these divisions.

   (a) $64 \div 3$   (b) $58 \div 4$   (c) $76 \div 8$   (d) $83 \div 4$   (e) $64 \div 7$

   (f) $47 \div 2$   (g) $85 \div 9$   (h) $53 \div 5$

4. A small hovercraft carries 26 passengers. This hovercraft makes 9 trips each morning.

   What is the greatest number of passengers that can be carried on this hovercraft in one morning?

5. A length of pastry, 96cm long, is cut into 6cm strips. How many strips can this 96cm length be cut into?

6. Adrienne's heart beats 69 times in 1 minute.

   How many times does it beat in 5 minutes?

7. Each coach owned by Greylines can carry 85 passengers.

   How many passengers can 7 of these coaches carry?

8. A box holds 6 eggs. 80 eggs are packed into these boxes.

   (a) How many boxes are completely filled?

   (b) How many eggs are in the box that is not completely filled?

9. Some taxis can carry 6 passengers.

   How many of these will be needed for 47 people?

10. Which costs more: 27 apples at 7p each or 23 peaches at 8p each?

11. Jon's car takes 6 minutes to make one circuit of a track.

How many circuits can be made in 1 hour 24 minutes?

12.

• 210

• 16

• 54

• 19

• 28

• 114

• 175

• 66

• 43

• 12

• 78

• 72

Trace this diagram into your book.

Find the answers to the calculations below. Join the dots in the order in which the answers appear.

1. $18 \times 4$    2. $11 \times 6$    3. $18 \times 3$    4. $25 \times 7$    5. $39 \times 2$

6. $19 \times 6$    7. $48 \div 4$    8. $95 \div 5$    9. $86 \div 2$    10. $27 \times 2$

11. $42 \times 5$    12. $84 \div 3$    13. $96 \div 6$    14. $35 \times 5$    15. $36 \times 2$

**Review 1**   Find the answer to these.

(a) $47 \times 9$    (b) $32 \times 7$    (c) $87 \div 3$    (d) $79 \div 2$    (e) $\frac{68}{4}$

**Review 2**   (a) 96 maths. books were bought for £8 each.

How much did they cost altogether?

(b) At the end of the year, another £96 was spent to buy more of these books.

How many more were bought?

## GAME 4:9

**CARD CALCULATIONS:** a game for 2 students.

**Equipment:** A pack of cards with the Jacks, Queens and Kings removed.

**The Play:** Decide which student will deal first.

The dealer shuffles and deals 4 cards, face up.

The other student tries to make a correct calculation using 3 or 4 of these cards. (Ace is 1.)

For instance, if these cards are dealt, the calculation $1 + 7 = 4 \times 2$ may be made.

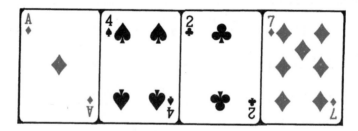

If the student uses all 4 cards for the calculation, 2 points are scored.

If just 3 cards are used, 1 point is scored.

If no calculation can be made, the dealer changes.

**Timing:** The winner is the student who has scored the most points after a set time, maybe 10 minutes.

## PUZZLE 4:10

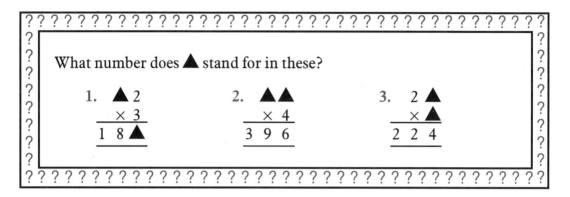

What number does ▲ stand for in these?

1.  ▲ 2
    × 3
   ─────
   1 8 ▲

2.  ▲▲
    × 4
   ─────
   3 9 6

3.  2 ▲
    × ▲
   ─────
   2 2 4

## READING and WRITING DECIMALS

The number 0·73 is read as zero point seven three.
Each digit after the decimal point is read separately.

The number 84·73 is read as eighty four point seven three.
That is, digits after the decimal point are read separately but digits before the point aren't.

## EXERCISE 4:11

1.  How are these numbers read?

    (a) 7·6        (b) 0·05        (c) 17·06        (d) 0·503

    (e) 271·50     (f) 21·003      (g) 0·95

2.  Write these numbers as decimals.

    (a) zero point seven one   *0·71*        (b) zero point one seven one

    (c) zero point one seven                 (d) seven point zero zero one

    (e) twenty point five two                (f) twenty five point zero two

    (g) five point five zero                 (h) zero point eight one zero

    (i) one hundred point one

*Calculation: pencil and paper methods*

**Review**   (a) 0·39      (b) 0·309      (c) 3·03      (d) 39·3

From the following list, choose the correct way of reading each of the above numbers.

A.  three point three

B.  zero point thirty nine

C.  zero point three zero nine

D.  three nine point three

E.  three point zero three

F.  zero point three nine

G.  thirty nine point zero three

H.  three zero three

I.  three nine point zero

J.  thirty nine point three

---

## DISCUSSION EXERCISE 4:12

0·73 is read as zero point seven three, not as zero point seventy three.
84·73 is read as eighty four point seven three, not as eighty four point seventy three.

How do you read £84·73?
How do you read £0·73?
Is money a special case?
Are there other measurements that are read in a similar way to money? **Discuss.**

---

## PUZZLE 4:13

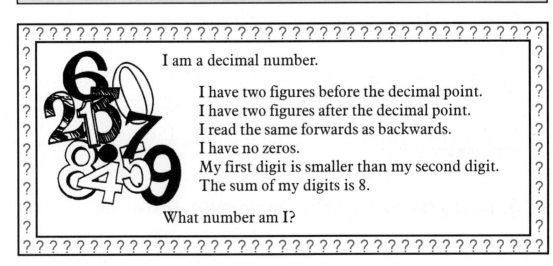

I am a decimal number.

I have two figures before the decimal point.
I have two figures after the decimal point.
I read the same forwards as backwards.
I have no zeros.
My first digit is smaller than my second digit.
The sum of my digits is 8.

What number am I?

62

# ADDING and SUBTRACTING DECIMALS: pencil and paper methods

## DISCUSSION EXERCISE 4:14

- To add 3·42 + 15·8, Nada set out her working as shown.

$$
\begin{array}{r}
3{\cdot}42 \\
+\,15{\cdot}8 \\
\hline
19{\cdot}22 \\
\end{array}
$$

She said that the 3 and the 5 must be lined up and added since these were both units.

How else could Nada have explained her setting out? **Discuss.**

Could 3·42 + 15·8 be set out in any other way? **Discuss.**

- To do the subtraction 7 – 1·2, Nada set out her working as shown.

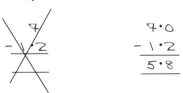

Why do you think Nada crossed out her first attempt? **Discuss.**

Could 7 – 1·2 be set out in any other way? **Discuss.**

- ⎡0·6 + 12·2⎤ Anne cycled 0·6km to Beth's house. Then Anne and Beth cycled 12·2km to the next village. Altogether Anne had cycled 12·8km.

Make up another "story" for the addition 0·6 + 12·2. **Discuss** your "story" with your group or class.

- ⎡7·34 – 1·25⎤ Make up a "story" for this subtraction.

**Discuss** your "story".

## EXERCISE 4:15

1. Find the answer to these.

    (a)    6·8      (b)    17·3      (c)    2·34      (d)    24·5      (e)    17·08
           + 2·5          + 2·6         + 8·9        + 18·84      + 5·57

    (f)   3·6 + 7·08      (g)   21·4 + 3·9      (h)   9·98 + 0·59      (i)   0·9 + 1·47

2. Do these subtractions.

    (a)    8·6      (b)    7·5      (c)    24·8      (d)    25·6      (e)    2·4
          − 3·4         − 2·7        − 8·9       − 8·92      − 0·54

    (f)   8·5 − 4·42      (g)   14 − 10·6      (h)   8 − 4·08      (i)   12·6 − 7

3. From a 2·5m plank, the lengths 0·8m and 1·6m are cut.

   What length of plank is left?

4. In a competition, a woman threw the shot 20·67m, 19·81m and 20·28m on her three attempts.

   How much longer was her best throw than her worst throw?

5. The temperature rose from 9·6°C at 9 a.m. to 15°C at 2 p.m.

   How much did the temperature rise?

6. Find the answers to these.

    (a)   £71·64 + £107·05      (b)   4·6 kg + 14·08 kg      (c)   0·59 km + 7·7 km

    (d)   £2·95 + 80p      (e)   1·8m + 0·5m + 4·05m      (f)   1·2*l* − 0·55*l*

    (g)   95p + 78p − £1·24      (h)   64g + 25·5g − 45·8g

7. Marion needed 127·4m of timber to build a deck. She bought 36·2m and then another 27·3m.

   How much more did Marion need to buy?

8. When interest of £5·49 was added to Nuria's bank account the total was £84·02.

   How much was in Nuria's bank account before the interest was added?

9. Tim bought three short ends of material to make a jacket. These measured 1·55m, 1·9m and 1·75m. Altogether Tim used 3·95m to make his jacket.

   How much material did Tim have left over?

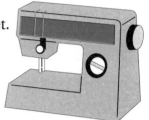

10. Last weekend, Anthony's family made four short journeys in their car. These were 6·8 km, 10·7 km, 9 km and 4·4 km. At the end of the weekend the reading on the speedometer was 69435·1 km.

    What was the reading before the weekend?

**Review 1**    Copy and complete this crossnumber.

**Across**
1. 7·5 − 6·3
3. 4 − 2·7
5. 0·23 + 0·17
6. 66·8 + 33·2
8. 395·5 + 60·5
10. 186·45 + 88·55
12. 45·88 + 254·12
14. 10 − 9·9
15. 12·1 − 3·7
16. 5·2 − 3·4

**Down**
1. 1·85 − 0·75
2. 189·2 + 10·8
3. 143·56 + 0·44
4. 4·2 − 0·6
7. 1·4 − 0·7
9. 2·63 + 2·37
10. 0·81 + 1·2 + 0·79
11. 298·51 + 201 + 4·49
12. 60·13 + 250·87
13. 3·5 + 13·08 − 15·78

**Review 2**    An empty lorry weighs 4·26 tonne. When this lorry is loaded with wheat its weight is 11·4 tonne.

   How much wheat is on this lorry?

## PUZZLE 4:16

?????????????????????????????????????????
$36 + 12 = 372$        $136 - 4 = 96$        $281 + 12 - 145 = 31$

Where should the decimal points be placed to make these true?

Is there more than one answer?
?????????????????????????????????????????

## INVESTIGATION 4:17

### DECIMAL MAGIC SQUARES

1. The numbers in this magic square have been mixed up. Change the numbers around so that the sum of each row, each column and each diagonal is 3·3.

   Can this be done in more than one way? **Investigate.**

   | 1·5 | 0·9 | 0·3 |
   |-----|-----|-----|
   | 0·7 | 1·3 | 1·7 |
   | 1·1 | 0·5 | 1·9 |

2. 

   | 1·9 |     |     |
   |-----|-----|-----|
   |     | 1·8 |     |
   |     |     | 1·7 |

   **Investigate** ways of finishing this magic square.

3. Is this a magic square?
   Would it be a magic square if each number had a decimal point?
   **Investigate.**

   | 155 | 150 | 250 | 125 |
   |-----|-----|-----|-----|
   | 450 | 105 | 95  | 750 |
   | 850 | 65  | 550 | 115 |
   | 350 | 135 | 145 | 50  |

4. Make up your own magic square using decimal numbers.

# INVESTIGATION 4:18

## DECIMAL PATHS

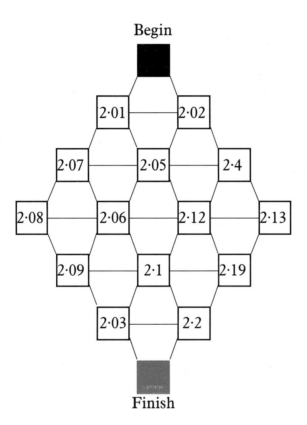

Begin

2·01 — 2·02

2·07 — 2·05 — 2·4

2·08 — 2·06 — 2·12 — 2·13

2·09 — 2·1 — 2·19

2·03 — 2·2

Finish

**Investigate** paths from the black square to the red square.

You could investigate one of the following or something different.

- the sums of the paths that go through exactly 7 numbers

- the paths that have the same total

- the greatest difference between any two paths that go through the same number of boxes

## PRACTICAL EXERCISE 4:19

1.  Make a mural for your classroom wall showing decimals being used in everyday life.

    You could cut and paste pictures and diagrams from newspapers, brochures or magazines. You could draw your own pictures and diagrams.

2.  Plan a cycling holiday for your family.

    Make a list of equipment, food and clothing needed. Find the cost of these. Also find the cost of any places you will stay or transport needed.

3.  Investigate the cost of owning a pet.
    You could make a poster of your investigation.

## PROJECT

The Roman number system is still used today.
The Chinese and Greeks had number systems of their own.
Use reference books to do a project on one of these number systems.

**DID YOU KNOW** that if the calculator display is turned upside down the numbers are quite similar to some of the letters of the alphabet?

Calculator display:

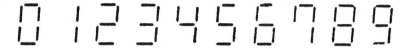

Upside down display:

Upper case letter:    O    I      E      S       L    B   G

## DISCUSSION EXERCISE 5:1

- SUE 34526 + 22582 AN 1000 − 7 FOR 1259 + 2514.

  What does this sentence read? Discuss.


- Make up a list of words using the upper case letters G, B, L, S, E, I, O.

  Discuss your list with your group.


  Use your list of words to make up sentences similar to that above. Try to replace every second word in your sentence with a calculation.

  Discuss your sentences with your neighbour or group.


- If the calculator display is turned upside down, some of the numbers are quite similar to lower case letters of the alphabet.
  What numbers are similar to h, g and b?
  Discuss.

69

- Crosswords can be made up using calculator clues.
  **Discuss** how this could be done.

  As part of your discussion, you may like to look at the part of this crossword that has been done.
  You may like to make up another small part of this crossword.

| | | | H | O | B |
|---|---|---|---|---|---|
| | | | | H | E |
| | | | | | L |
| | | | | | L |
| | | | | | |
| | | | | | |

**Across**
2.  800 + 4
5.
7.  43 − 9
8.
10.
12.
14.
15.

**Down**
1.
3.  8 × 5
4.  5231 + 2507
6.
8.
9.
11.
13.

## READING CALCULATOR DISPLAYS

There is a maximum number of digits that can be displayed on any calculator screen.
On a calculator with an 8-digit screen display, the answer to the division 7 ÷ 3 is displayed as 2·3333333. Other calculators may display more than, or fewer than, 8 digits.

We often need to give the answer to a calculation to the nearest whole number.

*Example*   A calculator displayed the answer to 7 ÷ 3 as 2·3333333.
To the nearest whole number, the answer to 7 ÷ 3 is 2.

*Example*   A calculator displayed the answer to 53 ÷ 7 as 7·5714286.
To the nearest whole number, the answer to 53 ÷ 7 is 8.

Sometimes we need to give the answer to a calculation to the closest but smaller whole number.

*Worked Example*   Apples are 13p each.
How many apples can be bought with 50p?

*Answer*   On the calculator, the answer to 50 ÷ 13 is 3·8461538.
Only 3 apples can be bought.

70

## DISCUSSION EXERCISE 5:2

In the previous worked example, the answer was given as the closest but smaller whole number.

Think of other examples where you might need to give the answer to the closest but smaller whole number. **Discuss** with your group or your class.

## EXERCISE 5:3

1. Give the following calculator displays to the nearest whole number.

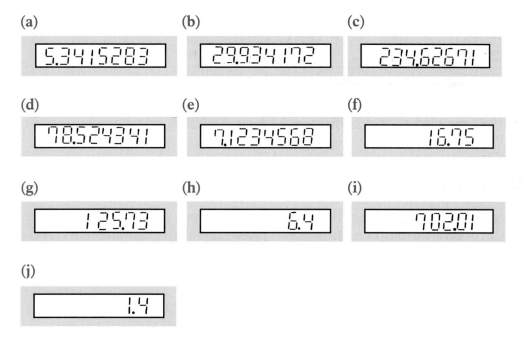

(a)  5.3415283

(b)  29.934172

(c)  234.62671

(d)  78.524341

(e)  7.1234568

(f)  16.75

(g)  125.73

(h)  6.4

(i)  702.01

(j)  1.4

2. Give the calculator displays in **question 1** to the closest but smaller whole number.

Review   Give this calculator display to

(a) the nearest whole number

(b) the closest but smaller whole number.

42.634898

---

## GAME 5:4

---

THE GAME of 31: a game for 2 students.

The aim of this game is to reach exactly 31.

The students take it in turn to key one of the numbers 1, 2, 3, 4, 5 or 6 followed by  + .

The first student to reach 31 is the winner.

A sample game is shown. (Anna won this game.)

| Anna | 6 + | | 5 + | | 3 + | | 6 + |
|---|---|---|---|---|---|---|---|
| James | | 4 + | | 6 + | | 1 + | |
| Calculator display | 6 | 10 | 15 | 21 | 24 | 25 | 31 |

---

## USING the CALCULATOR for CALCULATIONS

The calculator is often used for calculations. It is very useful when the numbers are large or have many digits.

Always have a rough idea of the size of the answer you expect to get. It is very easy to press a wrong key or to forget to press the = key at the end of a calculation.

*Worked Example*    Meals at "Maud's Carvery" cost £4.

(a) How many meals can be bought for £30?

(b) How much change will there be?

*Answer*    (a) We need to find 30 ÷ 4. **Key**  30 ÷ 4 =  to get a calculator display of 7·5.
7 meals can be bought.

(b) 7 meals cost 7 × £4 = £28.
Amount of change  = £30 − £28
= £2

*Worked Example*   Chocolate bars cost 23p each.
How much change is there from £5 if 13 of these are bought?

*Answer*   We need to find 13 × 23p.  **Key** $\boxed{13}\boxed{\times}\boxed{23}\boxed{=}$ to get a calculator display of 299.  Cost = 299p
= £2·99.

Amount of change = £5 – £2·99
= £2·01  (**Key** $\boxed{5}\boxed{-}\boxed{2.99}\boxed{=}$ )

## EXERCISE 5:5

1.   Steve's take-away meal cost £6·45. He used a £10 note to pay for this.

How much change did Steve get?

2.   Stephanie's car holds 54 litres of petrol. Petrol costs 42p per litre.

What is the cost of a full tank of petrol for Stephanie's car?

3.   This table gives the points given to 10 couples in a ballroom dancing competition.

| Couple No.<br>Dance | 23 | 98 | 47 | 125 | 72 | 121 | 7 | 58 | 64 | 92 |
|---|---|---|---|---|---|---|---|---|---|---|
| **Tango** | 7·25 | 5·95 | 6·00 | 5·45 | 7·05 | 6·25 | 9·10 | 6·35 | 7·15 | 5·75 |
| **Waltz** | 8·30 | 8·45 | 7·25 | 6·25 | 5·90 | 7·35 | 8·05 | 7·00 | 5·70 | 7·10 |
| **Quickstep** | 6·95 | 9·10 | 8·30 | 7·10 | 8·20 | 6·45 | 6·20 | 7·10 | 8·00 | 6·95 |

(a)  How many points did the Number 58 couple get in the waltz?

(b)  How many points did the Number 58 couple get altogether?

(c)  Which couple had the lowest total?

(d)  Which couple won this competition?

4.   Aileen won a race in a time of 23·8 seconds. Deborah's time was 0·35 seconds slower.

What was Deborah's time for the race?

5. **(a)** How many 19p chocolate bars can be bought with £5?

   **(b)** How much will be left over?

6. Brian is building a fence.
   He needs 125 lengths of timber, each 1·8m long. Altogether, he buys 200 metres of timber.

   Will Brian have enough?

7. Kylie is going to Belgium for a holiday.
   She buys £55 worth of Belgian francs.
   The exchange rate is 61 Belgian francs for £1.

   How many Belgian francs does Kylie buy?

   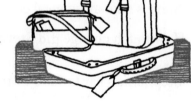

8. Munnah has £14·33 and Kate has £13·25.

   How much must Munnah give Kate for both girls to end up with the same amount?

9.

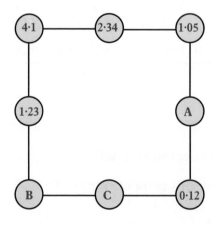

The three numbers along each side of this square must add to the same total.

What numbers must be placed in the circles A, B and C?

**Review 1**  In the Fifield rugby team, the three front row forwards weigh 66·2kg, 68·7kg and 73·5kg.
In the Newton team, these forwards weigh 69·7kg, 68·8kg and 69·1kg.

Which team has the heaviest front row and by how much?

**Review 2**  The 19 students in a class each gave 35p to buy a book for the library.
The book cost £8·50.

How much more was needed to buy this book?

**Review 3**  The weight of a lorry is 15400kg.
This lorry is loaded with 48 cartons, all of which weigh the same.
The weight of the loaded lorry is 21568kg.
What is the weight of each carton?

---

## PUZZLE 5:6

? ? ? ? ? ? ? ? ? ? ? ? ? ? ? ? ? ? ? ? ? ? ? ? ? ? ? ? ? ? ? ? ? ? ? ? ? ? ? ? ? ? ? ?

1.  ★ 2 ★ 2
   − 2 ★ 2 ★
   ─────────
    3 ★ 3 ★

   Replace the ★ with the same digit to make this subtraction correct.

2.     1111
       3333
       5555      Replace ten of the digits with 0 so that the sum
       7777      comes to 1111.
     + 9999
     ─────────

? ? ? ? ? ? ? ? ? ? ? ? ? ? ? ? ? ? ? ? ? ? ? ? ? ? ? ? ? ? ? ? ? ? ? ? ? ? ? ? ? ? ? ?

## INVESTIGATION 5:7

### KAPREKAR'S NUMBER (6174)

Begin with the 4-digit number 3259.

| | | |
|---|---|---|
| *Step 1* | Write the digits from largest to smallest | 9532 |
| | Write the digits from smallest to largest | − 2359 |
| | Subtract | 7173 |

*Step 2, . . .* Repeat **Step 1** with the new number.

That is **Step 2** is

$$
\begin{array}{r} 7731 \\ -\ 1377 \\ \hline 6354 \end{array}
$$

**Step 3** is

$$
\begin{array}{r} 6543 \\ -\ 3456 \\ \hline 3087 \end{array}
$$

**Step 4** is

$$
\begin{array}{r} 8730 \\ -\ 0378 \\ \hline 8352 \end{array}
$$

**Step 5** is

$$
\begin{array}{r} 8532 \\ -\ 2358 \\ \hline 6174 \end{array}
$$

At **Step 5** we reached Kaprekar's number.

What happens if we continue? That is, what is the answer at **Step 6, Step 7, . . .**?

Do we reach Kaprekar's number using this method with other 4-digit numbers? Investigate.

What if not all the digits are different?

## PRACTICAL EXERCISE 5:8

Plan a holiday abroad for your family.
Work out the cost of this holiday.

Include costs of travel, accommodation etc.
Include spending money.

Use the most recent exchange rate you can find.

## JUST FOR FUN

Ask a friend to key the following, pressing $\boxed{=}$ after each number is entered:

    Key the number of the month in which you were born.
    Multiply by 5.
    Add 7.
    Multiply by 4.
    Subtract 20.
    Multiply by 5.
    Add the day of the month on which you were born.
    Subtract 40.

Now look at your friend's calculator and tell your friend his or her birthdate.

For instance, if a person was born on the 18th of July the following will appear on the calculator display:

| 7 | 35 | 42 | 168 | 148 | 740 | 758 | 7 18 |
|---|----|----|-----|-----|-----|-----|------|
|   |    |    |     |     |     |     | ↑ ↑  |
|   |    |    |     |     |     |     | month day |

**DID YOU KNOW** that fractions and percentages are often used as a way of giving information?

## DISCUSSION EXERCISE 6:1

Defrost, 35% power

"1½ spoons of sugar please"

65% polyester
35% cotton

⅓ MORE FREE

100% WOOL

Mix ¼ cup oatmeal

⅔ cup water

⅛ tsp salt

Cook on High for 2½ minutes

HALF PRICE AFTER 8pm

"Half a glass please"

**Discuss** whether the meaning of these advertisements, labels and instructions is clear.

# FRACTIONS

$\frac{2}{5}$ is read as "two-fifths".

$\frac{2}{5}$ means 2 parts out of every 5.

For instance, $\frac{2}{5}$ of these dots are red.

## DISCUSSION EXERCISE 6:2

- One-half of each of these grids is shaded. How else could you shade one-half? **Discuss.**

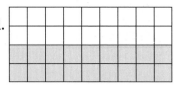 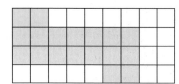

- Estimate how long $\frac{1}{4}$ of this line is. ▬▬▬▬▬▬

  **Discuss** how to decide if the estimate is reasonable.

- Draw other lines.

  Estimate fractions of these lines. Include fractions such as $\frac{1}{3}$, $\frac{2}{3}$, $\frac{3}{5}$ etc.

  **Discuss** your estimates with other members of your group.

- This container is partly filled with liquid.

  What fraction of the container is filled? **Discuss.**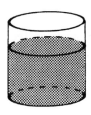

- Where are the following used? **Discuss.**

   quarter-final    half-time    half-price    half a head
  three-quarter length    one and a half lengths    wing three-quarters

  Think of other examples where fractions are used. **Discuss.**

- Aaron and Ali share an apple. Aaron says "my half is smaller". Is this possible? **Discuss.**

## PRACTICAL EXERCISE 6:3

1.  Bring empty containers to class.

    Fill them with water so they are $\frac{1}{2}$ full, $\frac{1}{4}$ full, $\frac{3}{4}$ full, $\frac{2}{5}$ full etc.

    **Discuss** how you could do this accurately.

2.

Choose a fraction, perhaps $\frac{1}{3}$ .

Try to find two objects where the length of one is $\frac{1}{3}$ the length of the other.

Repeat for other fractions such as $\frac{1}{5}$ , $\frac{2}{3}$ , $\frac{3}{4}$ etc.

3.  Find examples of fractions from newspapers or magazines or brochures.

    Display your collection on a poster or make a collage.

*Worked Example*     Gayle bought 6 jaffa cakes. She gave 4 of these to her friends.

   (a) What fraction of the jaffa cakes did Gayle give to her friends?

   (b) What fraction did she keep?

*Answer*     (a) Gayle gave $\frac{4}{6}$ to her friends.

   (b) Gayle kept 2 for herself. That is, she kept $\frac{2}{6}$.

## EXERCISE 6:4

1.

   What fraction of these animals is dogs?

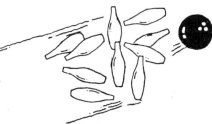

2. What fraction of these pins is lying down?

3. What fraction of these pictures is red?

   **(a)** 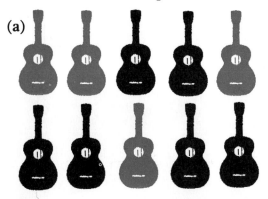          **(b)**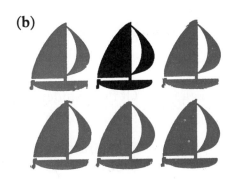

4. Rachel was away from school for 2 of the last 5 days.

   (a) What fraction of days was Rachel away from school?

   (b) What fraction of days was Rachel at school?

5. Of 8 friends, 5 play cricket.

   What fraction do not play cricket?

6. In each of the following words, what fraction of the letters is the letter A?

   (a) ELIZABETH          (b) MATHEMATICS          (c) FARUQ

7. Draw 6 copies of this grid.

Shade your copies to show the following fractions:

$\frac{3}{4}$, $\frac{3}{5}$, $\frac{7}{10}$; $\frac{7}{20}$, $\frac{1}{5}$, $\frac{1}{4}$.

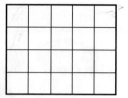

8. Brent surveyed 50 houses about heating. His results are shown.

What fraction of these houses **(a)** used gas

        **(b)** used oil

        **(c)** did not use gas?

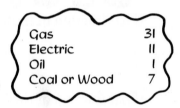

**Review 1**   What fraction of the dots is red?

      **(a)**           **(b)**           **(c)**           **(d)**

**Review 2**   Of the 6 students in Julia's group, only two are girls.

What fraction of Julia's group is boys?

## DISCUSSION EXERCISE 6:5

- Suppose 7 apples are to be shared between 2 people. How many apples does each get?

The division $\frac{7}{2}$ can be done as:    $2\overline{)7}$   $\begin{array}{c}3 \text{ with remainder of 1}\end{array}$

We can give the answer to this division as $\frac{7}{2} = 3\frac{1}{2}$.

Compare the division $\frac{7}{2}$ with the sharing of the apples. **Discuss.**

- "The answer to $\frac{47}{5}$ can be written as $9\frac{2}{5}$". **Discuss** this statement.

- "The answers to *all* divisions can be written as either a whole number or a whole number and a fraction". **Discuss** this statement.

Test many divisions such as $\frac{72}{8}$, $\frac{38}{6}$, $\frac{41}{10}$ etc. as part of your discussion.

## PUZZLE 6:6

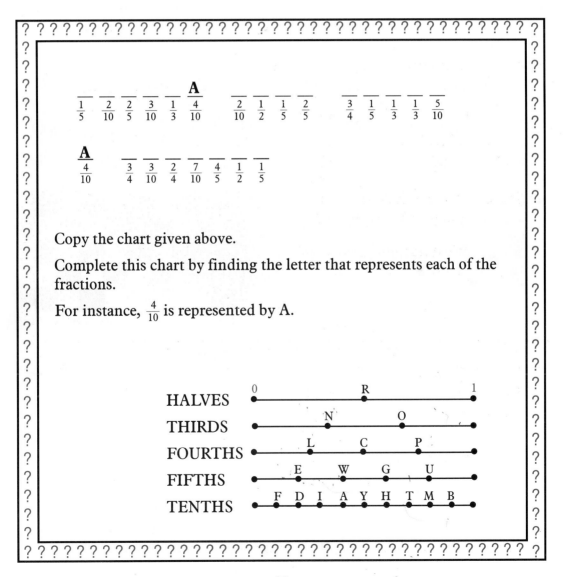

Copy the chart given above.

Complete this chart by finding the letter that represents each of the fractions.

For instance, $\frac{4}{10}$ is represented by A.

## PERCENTAGES

Fractions which are out of one hundred are often called **percentages.**

For instance, 4 out of 100 is $\frac{4}{100}$. This is also written as 4% and read as "4 per cent".

| DISCUSSION EXERCISE 6:7 |
|---|

- In each of the following squares, 70% has been shaded.

Discuss other ways in which 70% of a square could be shaded.

- What percentage of the above squares is not shaded? **Discuss.**

- What would the above squares look like if they were 100% shaded? **Discuss.** Could you shade more than 100%? **Discuss.**

- Christopher said "60% of my class are boys and 30% are girls". **Discuss** Christopher's statement.

- Jennifer said "100% of the students in my school are girls". **Discuss** Jennifer's statement.

- Simon said "30% of my friends have been to Italy, 45% have been to France and 50% have been to Spain so 125% of my friends have been abroad". **Discuss** Simon's statement.

- Make up a percentage statement. **Discuss** with your group.

*Worked Example*   On an airline, 3 out of every 100 passengers travelled first class.

    (a)  What percentage travelled first class?

    (b)  What percentage did not travel first class?

*Answer*   (a)  3%

    (b)  97 out of every 100 did not travel first class.
That is, 97% did not travel first class.

*Worked Example*   There were 5 events in a competition. Points were given out of 20 for each event. These were then added to give a total out of 100.

| Event | 1 | 2 | 3 | 4 | 5 |
|---|---|---|---|---|---|
| Kyle's team | 15 | 16 | 13 | 10 | 13 |
| Susan's team | 14 | 12 | 18 | 14 | 11 |

What percentages did Kyle's team and Susan's team get in this competition?

*Answer*   Total points out of 100 for Kyle's team = 67. Percentage = 67%
Total points out of 100 for Susan's team = 69. Percentage = 69%

## EXERCISE 6:8

1.  An exam. was out of 100.
    The marks of 6 students are shown.

    What percentage did each of these students get?

    | Beth  | 84 |
    |-------|----|
    | James | 77 |
    | Sarah | 79 |
    | Emma  | 62 |
    | Imran | 79 |
    | Brian | 68 |

2.  What percentage of each diagram is shaded?

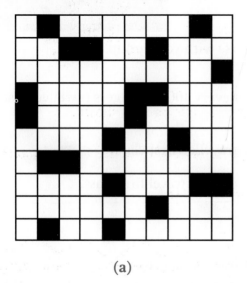
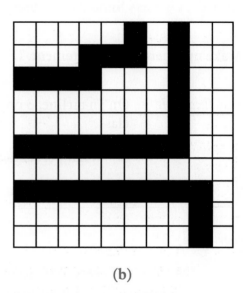

    (a)                                        (b)

3.  What percentage of each diagram in **question 2** is *not* shaded?

4.  A netball team won 80% of its games.

    What percentage did it not win?

5.  An advertisement for dog food says that all dogs like this food.

    If this is correct, what percentage like this food?

6.  If 27% of families have a home computer, what percentage do not?

7. A class raised money to give to charity.
   35% of the class wanted the money to go to the RSPCA. 40% wanted the money to go to Cancer Research.

   What percentage of the class wanted the money to go to something other than the RSPCA or Cancer Research?

8. A football team won 60% of their matches and drew 30%.

   What percentage of matches did they lose?

9.

| A. Bunn | 31% |
| C. Davidson | 14% |
| E. Fawke | |
| G. Hann | 7% |
| I. Jacobs | 18% |

The results of an election are shown.

(a) What percentage of votes did E. Fawke get?

(b) Who won the election?

**Review 1** The students who had been on an Outdoor Activities week filled in a questionnaire at the end of the week.
The results of a question on the favourite activity are shown. The percentage who liked orienteering best is missing.

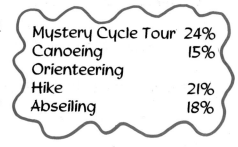

Mystery Cycle Tour 24%
Canoeing 15%
Orienteering
Hike 21%
Abseiling 18%

What percentage of students liked orienteering best?

**Review 2** Each person in a diving competition had 5 dives.
Points, out of 20, were given for each dive.

Tim's results are shown.
What percentage of the total points did Tim get?

| Dive | 1 | 2 | 3 | 4 | 5 |
|---|---|---|---|---|---|
| Points | 9 | 13 | 11 | 17 | 15 |

## PRACTICAL EXERCISE 6:9

1. Collect examples of percentages from newspapers, magazines or brochures. Put these into groups such as food, clothing, travel etc.

   Display your examples on a poster or a wall chart.

2. Where are percentages used in your other subjects? Find at least three examples.

   Write a few sentences about each of these examples. If you wish, you could draw a picture or a diagram for each example.

3. Make many different patterns by shading 20% of a square.

   If you wish, you could choose a percentage other than 20%.

Quantities out of a number other than 100 can be given as percentages.

To write a quantity out of 50 as a percentage, multiply by 2.

To write a quantity out of 25 as a percentage, multiply by 4.

To write a quantity out of 20 as a percentage, multiply by 5.

To write a quantity out of 10 as a percentage, multiply by 10.

To write a quantity out of 5 as a percentage, multiply by 20.

To write a quantity out of 4 as a percentage, multiply by 25.

To write a quantity out of 2 as a percentage, multiply by 50.

*Worked Example*   In Amanda's survey on cars, she found that 29 out of 50 cars had one passenger. What percentage was this?

*Answer*   29 out of 50 is 29 × 2 out of 100. That is, 58 out of 100.
That is, 58% of cars had one passenger.

## EXERCISE 6:10

1. What percentage of these diagrams is shaded?

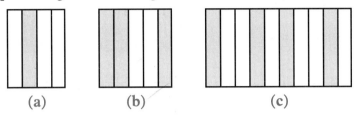

(a)          (b)          (c)

2.

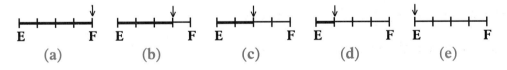

Find a percentage from the box for each statement.

(a) Seven out of ten people watch the news on TV.

(b) One out of every two people who eat at McDonald's is under 12.

(c) In a survey, it was found that maths. was the favourite subject of three-quarters of students.

(d) Two out of every five people go abroad for their summer holiday.

(e) Six out of every twenty students play a musical instrument.

3. These diagrams show how much petrol there is in the tank of a car.

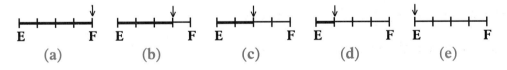

What percentage of a full tank is there in each case? E is empty. F is full.

4. Last week, Alex had tests in three of her subjects.
   She got   74% for Geography
             18 out of 25 for Mathematics
             16 out of 20 for Science.

   Which subject did Alex do best in? What percentage did she get in this subject?

5. If the Sands Hotel is full, it can hold 200 guests.

   How many guests were in this hotel on   (a) Jan 1st

   (b) April 1st

   (c) July 1st

   (d) Oct 1st?

| Occupancy Rate | |
| --- | --- |
| Jan 1st | 59% |
| April 1st | 64% |
| July 1st | 75% |
| Oct 1st | 72% |

6. (a) 5p in 100p. What percentage is this?

   (b) 5p in £1. What percentage is this?

   (c) 15p in £1. What percentage is this?

   (d) 17·5p in £1. What percentage is this?

7. Denise earns 10% on all the books she sells. What does she earn on the sale of a book worth   (a) £1   (b) £8   (c) £20?

8. If VAT is 17·5%, what is the VAT on each of these?

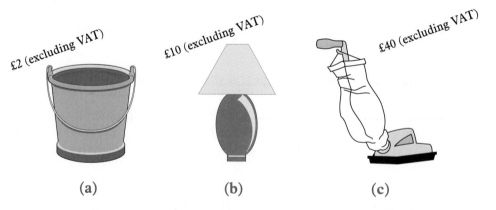

£2 (excluding VAT)   £10 (excluding VAT)   £40 (excluding VAT)

   (a)          (b)          (c)

**Review**   Megan got these marks in four tests.

   Number   15 out of 20
   Algebra   33 out of 50
   Shape, Space, Measures   17 out of 25
   Handling Data   7 out of 10

   In which of these tests did Megan do best? What was her percentage mark in this subject?

**JUST FOR FUN**

Can you answer these problems?

1.  The head of a fish is 4cm long.
    The body is as long as the head and tail together.
    The tail is as long as the head and half the body.
    How long is the fish?

2.  Half a number and twice half the number is two more than twice
    half the number.

    What is the number?

**DO NOT use your calculator for questions 1 to 15.**

1.

What fraction of these diagrams is red?

2. Write the following as figures.

   (a) twenty-five thousand and seventeen

   (b) seventy million, two hundred and fifteen thousand, seven hundred and two

   (c) twenty point zero three

3. Copy and complete this crossnumber.

| | Across | Down |
|---|---|---|
| | 1.  6 × 8 | 1.  246 + 165 |
| | 2.  281 + 34 + 376 | 2.  946 − 254 |
| | 4.  8 + 4 + 2 + 5 | 3.  50 ÷ 5 |
| | 5.  7 × 2 | 6.  5 × 9 |
| | 7.  3 × 9 | 8.  105 − 28 |
| | 9.  39 + 19 | 10.  1001 − 138 |
| | 11.  9 × 8 | 12.  198+74 |
| | 14.  8 × 8 | 13.  96 ÷ 6 |
| | 15.  345 + 348 | |
| | 16.  96 ÷ 3 | |

4. Angela saved £200 for her holiday.
   Her travel cost £38 and her hotel cost £77.

   How much did Angela have left for spending money?

5. Which of these problems has too much information and which has not enough?

   Find the answer to the problems if it is possible to do so.

   (a) Amanda and Rob collect stamps.
   Amanda has 145 stamps. Rob has 127.
   Rob buys another 17 stamps and gives 5 of these to Amanda.

   How many stamps does Amanda then have?

   (b) Jill made Christmas cards to give to her friends.
   She gave 9 to her friends at school and posted the rest.

   How many Christmas cards did Jill make?

6. What is the place value of the 9 in these?

   (a) 3944    (b) 194352    (c) 239    (d) 9234156    (e) 239400

7. The area of England is about 60% of Great Britain.

   What percentage of Great Britain is not England?

8. How many times larger is the 7 in 27941 than in 94271?

9. Christmas crackers are packed 8 to a box.

   (a) How many crackers are in 35 boxes?

   (b) Joanne packs 89 of these crackers into boxes.

   How many complete boxes can she fill?

   How many crackers will be left over?

10. (a) How many days are there in 8 complete weeks?

    (b) How many complete weeks are there in 28 days?

11. Use a place value chart to find the answer to these.

    (a) $71 \times 100$      (b) $13 \times 10$      (c) $400 \div 10$      (d) $125000 \div 100$

12. Copy and complete these addition and multiplication squares.

| + | 24 | 18 | 79 |
|---|---|---|---|
| 32 | 56 | | |
| 49 | | | |
| 67 | | | |

| + | 153 | 389 | |
|---|---|---|---|
| 221 | | | 364 |
| | | | 731 |
| | | | 210 |

| × | 3 | | 7 |
|---|---|---|---|
| | | 30 | |
| 4 | | 20 | |
| | | | 42 |

(a)                    (b)                    (c)

13. Write down the number that is  (a) ten less than 159

                                    (b) one hundred more than 3941

                                    (c) ten times as large as 326

                                    (d) one hundred times as large as 26

                                    (e) ten times smaller than 1600.

14. One of these is wrong. Which one?

    (a) $8347 > 7348$      (b) $231 < 312$      (c) $999 > 1000$      (d) $1452 < 1524$

15. Denford School had a Christmas pantomime.
    The income and expenses are shown below.

| Income | |
|---|---|
| Ticket sales | £545·50 |
| Programme sales | £28·00 |
| Sweet stall | £87·45 |

| Expenses | |
|---|---|
| Ticket and programme printing | £60·75 |
| Costume hire | £55·00 |
| Set and special lighting | £184·00 |
| Ingredients for sweets | £24·25 |

(a) What was the total income?

(b) What was the profit?

**For questions 16 to 30, you may use your calculator.**

16. Alexander Bell invented the telephone 24 years after Samuel Morse invented Morse Code.

    If Morse Code was invented in 1852, when was the telephone invented?

17.

(a) Which organisation had the greatest number of members in 1988?

(b) Which organisations had fewer members in 1988 than in 1971?

(c) Complete this list, placing the organisations in order of their membership size.

1971 Sea Cadet Corp, Rangers/ Young Leaders, . . .

| 14.2 Selected organisations for young people | | |
|---|---|---|
| *United Kingdom* | | Thousands |
| | | Members |
| | 1971 | 1988 |
| **Membership** | | |
| Beaver Scouts | | 98 |
| Cub Scouts | 265 | 254 |
| Scouts | 194 | 169 |
| Venture Scouts | 22 | 39 |
| Rainbow Guides | | 48 |
| Brownie Guides | 377 | 376 |
| Girl Guides | 295 | 233 |
| Rangers/Young Leaders | 21 | 27 |
| Sea Cadet Corps | 18 | 15 |
| Army Cadet Force | 39 | 42 |
| Air Training Corps | 33 | 39 |
| Combined Cadet Force | 45 | 43 |
| Boys' Brigade | 140 | 116 |
| Girls' Brigade | 97 | 81 |
| National Association of Boys Clubs | 164 | 166 |
| *Source: Key Data 1990/91* | | |

18. Mozart was five when he wrote "Twinkle Twinkle Little Star." Thirty years later, in 1791, he wrote "The Magic Flute."

    When was Mozart born?

19. Find the answer to these.

    (a) 2·6m + 3·5m      (b) 6·8cm – 0·34cm      (c) $7l - 2·4l$

    (d) 68g + 24·6g + 14·8g      (e) 7·1m – 5·2m – 1·3m      (f) £3·41 + 28p – 99p

20. Michael got these points for his Gymnastics badge.

| beam | 8·3 |
|------|-----|
| vault | 9·1 |
| floor | 8·8 |
| mat | 7·3 |
| bar | 9·0 |

(a) What was Michael's total score?

(b) If Allan got a total of 43·4, by how much did he beat Michael?

21.

| Walk | Cycle | Bus | Train | Car |
|------|-------|-----|-------|-----|
| 47% | 7% | 22% | | 7% |

This table shows how the students at Overleigh School come to school.

What percentage   (a) come to school by train

(b) either walk or cycle to school

(c) do not come to school by bus?

22. In a darts game, each player begins with 301 points.
The scores are subtracted from 301.
Elizabeth scores the following on her first six turns.

      Elizabeth:    39,   74,   38,   42,   35,   62

How many points must she score on her next turn to make her total exactly zero?

23. Jillian won the high jump competition with a best jump of 1·43m. This was 0·15m higher than Hannah's best jump.

How high was Hannah's best jump?

24. What percentage of each of these is shaded?

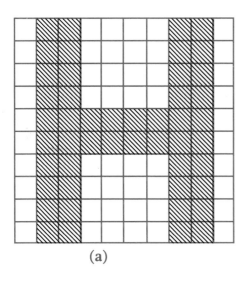

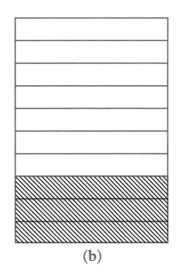

(a)                                    (b)

25. What fraction of each diagram in **question 24** is shaded?

26. Lemons cost 14p each.

    (a) How many can be bought with £1?

    (b) How much change will there be?

27. Of the 12 practice darts thrown by Julia, 5 landed on a double.

    What fraction of these darts did not land on a double?

28. In an exam. room, 30 desks are arranged in 6 rows.

    (a) How many desks are in each row?

    (b) How else could these desks be arranged if each row must have the same number of desks?

29. The difference between two numbers is 29.

    (a) If the larger is 91, find the smaller.

    (b) If the smaller is 135, find the larger.

30. Use the digits 4, 5, 6, 7, 8, 9 to make two 3-digit numbers which have a sum of 1542.

    Is there more than one answer?

# ALGEBRA

**DID YOU KNOW** that patterns occur all around us?

---

### DISCUSSION EXERCISE 8:1

The calendar for November 1993 is shown.

| S | M | T | W | T | F | S |
|---|---|---|---|---|---|---|
|   | 1 | 2 | 3 | 4 | 5 | 6 |
| 7 | 8 | 9 | 10 | 11 | 12 | 13 |
| 14 | 15 | 16 | 17 | 18 | 19 | 20 |
| 21 | 22 | 23 | 24 | 25 | 26 | 27 |
| 28 | 29 | 30 | | | | |

● Take any square of four numbers. For instance

| 1 | 2 |
|---|---|
| 8 | 9 |

Add the numbers on each diagonal. For instance $1 + 9 = 10$, $2 + 8 = 10$. Multiply the numbers on each diagonal and subtract. For instance, $2 \times 8 = 16$, $1 \times 9 = 9$ and $16 - 9 = 7$.

Repeat for other squares of four numbers. Discuss your results.

● Ask someone to give you the sum of three dates that are under one another. From this one piece of information, you can now name the three dates.

Discuss how you can do this.

● What patterns can you find in each of the three dotted parts? Discuss.

| S | M | T | W | T | F | S |
|---|---|---|---|---|---|---|
|   | 1 | 2 | 3 | 4 | 5 | 6 |
| 7 | 8 | 9 | 10 | 11 | 12 | 13 |
| 14 | 15 | 16 | 17 | 18 | 19 | 20 |
| 21 | 22 | 23 | 24 | 25 | 26 | 27 |
| 28 | 29 | 30 | | | | |

## PATTERNS in TABLES

**DISCUSSION EXERCISE 8:2**

●

| × | 1 | 2 | 3 | 4 | 5 |
|---|---|---|---|---|---|
| 1 | 1 | 2 | 3 | 4 | 5 |
| 2 | 2 | 4 | 6 | 8 | 10 |
| 3 | 3 | 6 | 9 | 12 | 15 |
| 4 | 4 | 8 | 12 | 16 | 20 |
| 5 | 5 | 10 | 15 | 20 | 25 |

Some of the patterns that can be found on this multiplication table are shown below. Look for symmetry and other patterns in your discussion.

| × | 1 | 2 | 3 | 4 | 5 |
|---|---|---|---|---|---|
| 1 | | | 3 | | |
| 2 | | | 6 | | |
| 3 | 3 | 6 | 9 | 12 | 15 |
| 4 | | | 12 | | |
| 5 | | | 15 | | |

**Discuss** the pattern here.

Are there similar patterns elsewhere on the table? **Discuss.**

| × | 1 | 2 | 3 | 4 | 5 |
|---|---|---|---|---|---|
| 1 | | | | | |
| 2 | | | 6 | 8 | 10 |
| 3 | | 6 | | | |
| 4 | | 8 | | | |
| 5 | | 10 | | | |

**Discuss** the positions of the numbers 6, 8, 10.

Are there similar patterns elsewhere on the table? **Discuss.**

Look back at the multiplication table at the top of this page.

How can you get the column 4, 8, 12, 16, 20 from the column 2, 4, 6, 8, 10? **Discuss.**

| × | 1 | 2 | 3 | 4 | 5 |
|---|---|---|---|---|---|
| 1 |   |   |   |   |   |
| 2 |   |   | 6 | 8 |   |
| 3 |   |   | 9 | 12 |   |
| 4 |   |   |   |   |   |
| 5 |   |   |   |   |   |

$6 \times 12 = 72$          $8 \times 9 = 72$

Is there a similar pattern in other squares of four numbers? **Discuss.**

- Write out the multiplication table up to $10 \times 10$.
  Look for patterns. **Discuss** the patterns you find.

- 

| + | 1 | 2 | 3 | 4 | 5 | 6 |
|---|---|---|---|---|---|---|
| 1 | 2 | 3 | 4 | 5 |   |   |
| 2 | 3 | 4 | 5 |   |   |   |
| 3 | 4 |   |   |   |   |   |
| 4 |   |   |   |   |   |   |

Write out the addition table up to $10 + 10$.

**Discuss** the patterns that you find.

## INVESTIGATION 8:3

### MAGIC SQUARE PATTERNS

The square of red numbers is a magic square. (Remember that all rows, all columns and both diagonals must add to the same number in a magic square.)

Is the large square also a magic square?

**Investigate** other magic squares within the large square.

| 11 | 18 | 13 | 74 | 81 | 76 | 29 | 36 | 31 |
|----|----|----|----|----|----|----|----|----|
| 16 | 14 | 12 | 79 | 77 | 75 | 34 | 32 | 30 |
| 15 | 10 | 17 | 78 | 73 | 80 | 33 | 28 | 35 |
| 56 | 63 | 58 | 38 | 45 | 40 | 20 | 27 | 22 |
| 61 | 59 | 57 | 43 | 41 | 39 | 25 | 23 | 21 |
| 60 | 55 | 62 | 42 | 37 | 44 | 24 | 19 | 26 |
| 47 | 54 | 49 | 2 | 9 | 4 | 65 | 72 | 67 |
| 52 | 50 | 48 | 7 | 5 | 3 | 70 | 68 | 66 |
| 51 | 46 | 53 | 6 | 1 | 8 | 69 | 64 | 71 |

# NUMBER PATTERNS

## DISCUSSION EXERCISE 8:4

- $$3 \times 11 = 33$$
  $$33 \times 11 = 363$$
  $$333 \times 11 = 3663$$
  $$3333 \times 11 = 36663$$

Discuss the pattern in the numbers 33, 363, 3663, 36663.

What do you think the answer to $33333 \times 11$ will be?
What do you think the answer to $33333333 \times 11$ will be? Discuss.

- $$33 \times 101 = 3333$$
  $$333 \times 101 = 33633$$
  $$3333 \times 101 = 336633$$

What do you think the answer to $33333 \times 101$ will be?
What do you think the answer to $3333333 \times 101$ will be? Discuss.

## EXERCISE 8:5

1. Copy and complete each number pattern. Use your calculator to do this.
   Use the number pattern to find the number in the box.

   (a) $2 \times 4 =$
   $22 \times 4 =$
   $222 \times 4 =$
   $2222 \times 4 =$

   $2222222 \times 4 = \square$

   (b) $4 \times 11 =$
   $44 \times 11 =$
   $444 \times 11 =$
   $4444 \times 11 =$

   $444444 \times 11 = \square$

   (c) $7 \times 6 =$
   $67 \times 66 =$
   $667 \times 666 =$
   $6667 \times 6666 =$

   $666667 \times 666666 = \square$

   (d) $22 \times 101 =$
   $222 \times 101 =$
   $2222 \times 101 =$
   $22222 \times 101 =$

   $\square \times 101 = 2244444422$

   (e) $4444 \div 44 =$
   $44844 \div 444 =$
   $448844 \div 4444 =$
   $4488844 \div 44444 =$

   $\square \div 444444 = 101$

2.
$$9 \times 5 = 45 \qquad 9 \times 6 = 54 \qquad 37 \times 99 = 3663$$
$$99 \times 55 = 5445 \qquad 99 \times 66 = 6534 \qquad 37 \times 999 = 36963$$
$$999 \times 555 = 554445 \qquad 999 \times 666 = 665334 \qquad 37 \times 9999 = 369963$$
$$9999 \times 5555 = 55544445 \qquad 9999 \times 6666 = 66653334 \qquad 37 \times 99999 = 3699963$$

Use these number patterns to find the answer to

(a) $9999999 \times 5555555$

(b) $999999 \times 666666$

(c) $37 \times 9999999$.

3.
$$1 \times 81 = 81$$
$$21 \times 81 = 1701$$
$$321 \times 81 = 26001$$
$$4321 \times 81 = 350001$$
$$54321 \times 81 = 4400001$$
$$654321 \times 81 = 53000001$$
$$7654321 \times 81 = 620000001$$
$$87654321 \times 81 = 7100000001$$

What is the number pattern in the answers?

Use this pattern to find the answer to $987654321 \times 81$.

4. (a) Copy and complete:
$$1089 \times 1 =$$
$$1089 \times 2 =$$
$$1089 \times 3 =$$
$$1089 \times 4 =$$
$$1089 \times 5 =$$
$$1089 \times 6 =$$

(b) Use the number pattern found in (a) to find the answer to these.
$$1089 \times 7 =$$
$$1089 \times 8 =$$
$$1089 \times 9 =$$

5. (a) Copy and complete:

| | |
|---|---|
| $9109 \times 1 = 9109$ | Sum of digits $= 9 + 1 + 0 + 9 = 19$ |
| $9109 \times 2 =$ | Sum of digits $= \qquad =$ |
| $9109 \times 3 =$ | Sum of digits $= \qquad =$ |
| $9109 \times 4 =$ | Sum of digits $= \qquad =$ |

(b) Use the number pattern found in (a) to find the sum of the digits in the answer to $9109 \times 8$.

6. Copy and complete:
$$1 = 1 = 1 \times 1$$
$$1 + 3 = 4 = 2 \times 2$$
$$1 + 3 + 5 = \ldots = 3 \times 3$$
$$1 + 3 + 5 + 7 = \ldots = \ldots$$
$$1 + 3 + 5 + 7 + 9 = \ldots = \ldots$$

**Review 1**   Copy and complete each number pattern.

Use the number pattern to find the number in the box.

(a)       $2 \times 3 =$          (b)       $9 \times 9 =$          (c)       $3333 \div 11 =$

$22 \times 3 =$                    $99 \times 99 =$                    $33633 \div 111 =$

$222 \times 3 =$                   $999 \times 999 =$                  $336633 \div 1111 =$

$2222 \times 3 =$                  $9999 \times 9999 =$                $3366633 \div 11111 =$

$222222 \times 3 = \square$        $99999 \times 99999 = \square$        $\square \div 1111111 = 303$

**Review 2**   Copy and complete:

$$2 \qquad\qquad = 2 = 1 \times 2$$
$$2 + 4 \qquad\qquad = \ldots = 2 \times 3$$
$$2 + 4 + 6 \qquad\qquad = 12 = 3 \times \ldots$$
$$2 + 4 + 6 + 8 \qquad = \ldots = \ldots \times \ldots$$
$$2 + 4 + 6 + 8 + 10 \quad = \ldots = \ldots \times \ldots$$

## INVESTIGATION 8:6

### NUMBER PATTERNS

1.  **Investigate** the number pattern made when 10101 is multiplied by any two-digit number.

2.  **Investigate** the number pattern made when 37 is multiplied by each of 3, 6, 9, 12, 15, 18, 21, 24, 27, . . .

    **What if** 74 was multiplied by each of 3, 6, 9, 12, . . .
    **What if** 148 was multiplied by each of 3, 6, 9, 12, . . .

3.  **Investigate** the number pattern made when 142857 is multiplied by each of 1, 3, 2, 6, 4, 5.

4.  Can you find other numbers which will give number patterns similar to those in **questions 1, 2, 3, or 4** of Exercise 8:5? **Investigate.**

# PATTERNS in DIAGRAMS

**DISCUSSION EXERCISE 8:7**

Discuss ways of finishing the third row of this pattern.

Discuss ways of finishing the fourth row of this pattern.

*Worked Example*

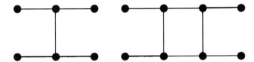 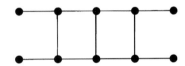

(a) Draw the next diagram in this pattern.

(b) How many vertical strokes and how many dots will there be in the tenth diagram in this pattern?

*Answer*    (a)

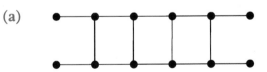

(b)

| Diagram | Vertical Strokes | Number of Dots |
|---------|------------------|----------------|
| 1st | 1 | $6 = 4 + 2$ |
| 2nd | 2 | $8 = 4 + 2 + 2$ |
| 3rd | 3 | $10 = 4 + 2 + 2 + 2$ |
| 4th | 4 | $12 = 4 + 2 + 2 + 2 + 2$ |

In the tenth diagram there will be 10 vertical strokes.

There will be $4 + 2 + 2 + 2 + 2 + 2 + 2 + 2 + 2 + 2 + 2 = 24$ dots.

## EXERCISE 8:8

1. Draw the next diagram in these patterns.

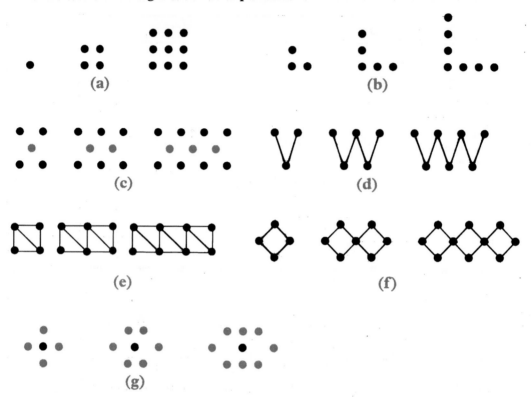

2. In words, describe the eighth diagram in each of the above patterns.

3. How many dots and how many strokes will there be in the eighth diagram in each of the above patterns?

4. Make up some dot patterns of your own. Describe them.

**Review**

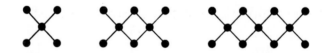

    (a) Draw the next diagram in this pattern.

    (b) How many strokes and how many dots will there be in the seventh diagram in this pattern?

# INVESTIGATION 8:9

## MATCHSTICK PATTERNS

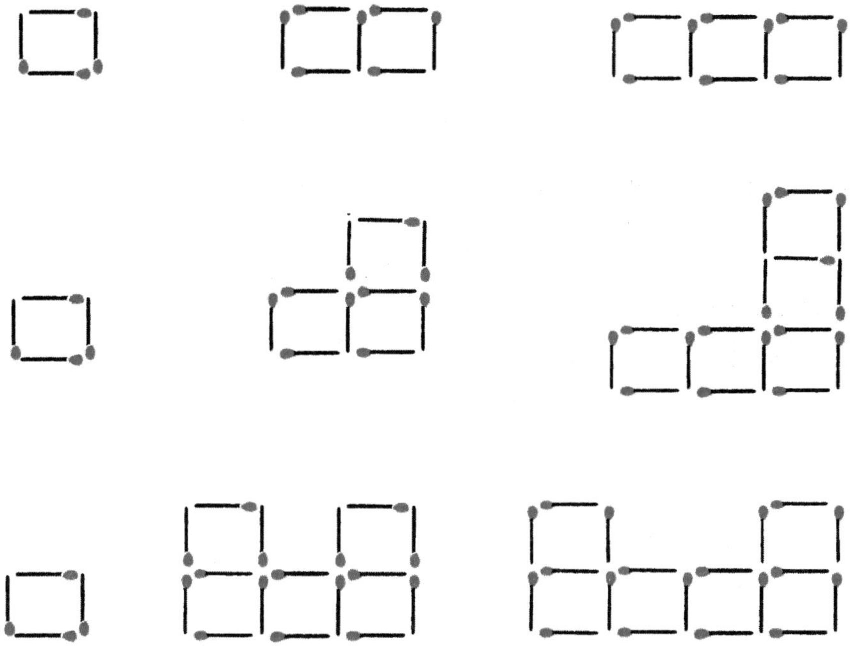

Some of the patterns that can be made by building matchstick squares are shown above.

**Investigate** other ways of building matchstick square patterns.

As part of your investigation, list the number of squares and the number of matchsticks used.

You may like to make other matchstick shapes such as the triangles shown below.

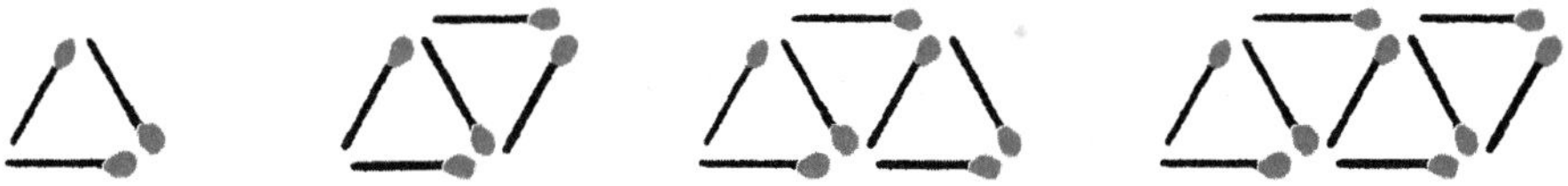

# DIVISIBILITY TESTS

A number is divisible by 2 if it is an even number.

A number is divisible by 3 if the sum of its digits is divisible by 3. For instance, 3429 is divisible by 3 since $3 + 4 + 2 + 9 = 18$ and 18 is divisible by 3.

A number is divisible by 4 if the number made from the last two digits is divisible by 4. For instance, 21012348 is divisible by 4 since 48 is divisible by 4.

A number is divisible by 5 if its last digit is 0 or 5.

A number is divisible by 6 if it is divisible by both 2 and 3.

A number is divisible by 8 if the number made from the last three digits is divisible by 8. For instance, 148168 is divisible by 8 since 168 is.

A number is divisible by 9 if the sum of its digits is divisible by 9. For instance, 77067 is divisible by 9 since $7 + 7 + 0 + 6 + 7 = 27$ which is divisible by 9.

## INVESTIGATION 8:10

### DIVISIBILITY of NUMBERS

1. Test the statements given above on some 2-digit numbers; some 3-digit, some 4-digit and some 5-digit numbers.

2. A number is divisible by 11 if the sum of the numbers made by "pairing" from the right is divisible by 11.
   For instance, 572 paired and added is $72 + 5 = 77$ which is divisible by 11. For instance, 284669 paired and added is $69 + 46 + 28 = 143$ which is divisible by 11.

   There is another way of testing if a number is divisible by 11.

   **Investigate** by making and testing statements. (*Hint*: Look at every second digit.)

## PRIME NUMBERS

A number which is divisible by only two numbers, itself and 1, is called a prime number.

The first few prime numbers are 2, 3, 5, 7, 11.

1 is not a prime number, since it is not divisible by two numbers.

## EXERCISE 8:11

1. In each of these lists there is one number which is not a prime number. Which number is this?

   (a) 1, 2, 3, 5, 7       (b) 2, 3, 5, 7, 9, 11       (c) 7, 11, 13, 17, 27

   (d) 2, 5, 11, 18, 23       (e) 17, 23, 29, 37, 39

2.

| 1 | 2 | 3 | 4 | 5 | 6 | 7 | 8 | 9 | 10 |
|---|---|---|---|---|---|---|---|---|---|
| 11 | 12 | 13 | 14 | 15 | 16 | 17 | 18 | 19 | 20 |
| 21 | 22 | 23 | 24 | 25 | 26 | 27 | 28 | 29 | 30 |
| 31 | 32 | 33 | 34 | 35 | 36 | 37 | 38 | 39 | 40 |
| 41 | 42 | 43 | 44 | 45 | 46 | 47 | 48 | 49 | 50 |
| 51 | 52 | 53 | 54 | 55 | 56 | 57 | 58 | 59 | 60 |
| 61 | 62 | 63 | 64 | 65 | 66 | 67 | 68 | 69 | 70 |
| 71 | 72 | 73 | 74 | 75 | 76 | 77 | 78 | 79 | 80 |
| 81 | 82 | 83 | 84 | 85 | 86 | 87 | 88 | 89 | 90 |
| 91 | 92 | 93 | 94 | 95 | 96 | 97 | 98 | 99 | 100 |

This is called "The Sieve of Eratosthenes."

Copy the number square. Do these instructions in the order in which they are given.

Cross out 1.
Cross out all the numbers which are divisible by 2, except 2 itself.
Cross out all the numbers which are divisible by 3, except 3 itself.
Cross out all the numbers which are divisible by 5, except 5 itself.
Cross out all the numbers which are divisible by 7, except 7 itself.

What do you notice about the numbers that are left?

3. Begin at any number on the bottom row and climb to the top of this "pyramid."

You may go through just one number at each level and each number you go through must be a prime.

Is there more than one route?

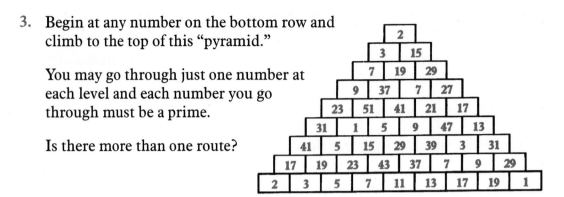

## Review

| 5 | 2 | 7 | 1 | 53 | 1 | 2 | 1 | 79 | 7 | 1 | 39 | 11 | 37 | 1 | 2 | 51 | 29 | 1 | 15 | 2 | 59 |
|---|---|---|---|----|---|---|---|----|---|---|----|----|----|---|---|----|----|---|----|---|----|
| 1 | 3 | 9 | 35 | 61 | 55 | 61 | 25 | 83 | 27 | 9 | 51 | 7 | 33 | 21 | 43 | 9 | 89 | 51 | 9 | 53 | 33 |
| 51 | 23 | 1 | 33 | 7 | 83 | 5 | 9 | 5 | 97 | 1 | 21 | 37 | 2 | 9 | 97 | 57 | 19 | 21 | 45 | 5 | 23 |
| 9 | 31 | 25 | 9 | 11 | 9 | 47 | 15 | 2 | 57 | 51 | 9 | 5 | 9 | 25 | 47 | 21 | 2 | 9 | 27 | 29 | 35 |
| 15 | 53 | 39 | 21 | 23 | 51 | 31 | 1 | 3 | 11 | 21 | 1 | 3 | 27 | 33 | 7 | 25 | 11 | 83 | 1 | 47 | 11 |

Copy this number grid.

Shade the squares with prime numbers.

What pattern does the shading give? (*Hint:* look for two words.)

## PUZZLES 8:12

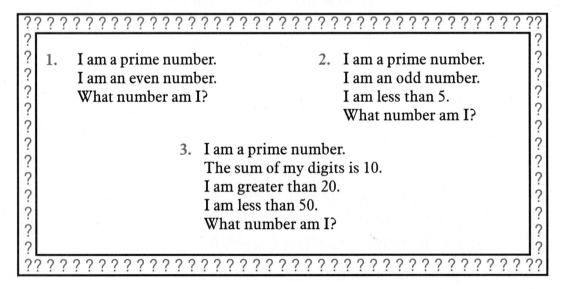

1. I am a prime number.
   I am an even number.
   What number am I?

2. I am a prime number.
   I am an odd number.
   I am less than 5.
   What number am I?

3. I am a prime number.
   The sum of my digits is 10.
   I am greater than 20.
   I am less than 50.
   What number am I?

## INVESTIGATION 8:13

### PRIMES

1.  **Investigate** prime numbers.

    You might like to test one of the following statements to see if it is true or false.   You may like to make and test a statement of your own.

    *Statement 1*   Every number can be written as the sum of two prime numbers.

    *Statement 2*   Every odd number, greater than 7, can be written as the sum of three prime numbers.

    **Emirp** numbers are prime numbers which give a different prime number when the digits are reversed. How is the word "emirp" related to the word "prime"?

    *Statement 3*   There are eight 2-digit emirp numbers.

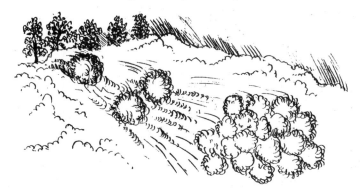

2.  2, 23, 239 is a list of **Snowball prime numbers.** All of these are prime numbers. The next number in this list would have 4 digits, the first 3 digits being 239.
    3, 31, 317 is another list of snowball prime numbers as is 7, 73, 733.

    How many lists (each three numbers long) of snowball prime numbers are there? **Investigate.**

    **What if** the lists were four numbers long?

## MULTIPLES

The **multiples** of a number are found by multiplying the number by each of 1, 2, 3, 4, 5, . . .

*Example*   The first six multiples of 4 are found by calculating
4 × 1, 4 × 2, 4 × 3, 4 × 4, 4 × 5, 4 × 6.
These are 4, 8, 12, 16, 20, 24.

## INVESTIGATION 8:14

### MULTIPLE PATTERNS

| 1 | 2 | 3 | 4 | 5 | 6 | 7 | 8 | 9 | 10 |
|---|---|---|---|---|---|---|---|---|----|
| 11 | 12 | 13 | 14 | 15 | 16 | 17 | 18 | 19 | 20 |
| 21 | 22 | 23 | 24 | 25 | 26 | 27 | 28 | 29 | 30 |
| 31 | 32 | 33 | 34 | 35 | 36 | 37 | 38 | 39 | 40 |
| 41 | 42 | 43 | 44 | 45 | 46 | 47 | 48 | 49 | 50 |
| 51 | 52 | 53 | 54 | 55 | 56 | 57 | 58 | 59 | 60 |
| 61 | 62 | 63 | 64 | 65 | 66 | 67 | 68 | 69 | 70 |
| 71 | 72 | 73 | 74 | 75 | 76 | 77 | 78 | 79 | 80 |
| 81 | 82 | 83 | 84 | 85 | 86 | 87 | 88 | 89 | 90 |
| 91 | 92 | 93 | 94 | 95 | 96 | 97 | 98 | 99 | 100 |

The numbers 1 to 100 are written on the grid.

The multiples of 2 are shown in red.
The multiples of 2 make a pattern. All the numbers in every second column are multiples of 2.

**Investigate** the pattern made when the multiples of 5 are coloured.

**What if** the multiples of 4 are coloured?

**What if** the multiples of 3 are coloured?

**What if** . . .

The calculator can be used to find multiples. This is done using multiplication by a constant.

*Example*   To find the first three multiples of 4:

**Key**   4  ×  ×  1  =  2  =  3  =

Key this yourself to get  4, 8, 12.

## EXERCISE 8:15

1.  Use your calculator to find the first five multiples of

(a) 6        (b) 7        (c) 8        (d) 9        (e) 10.

2.  Give the multiples of 6 that are

(a) less than 13     (b) less than 20     (c) between 13 and 20.

3.

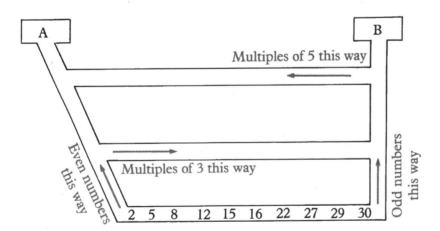

Follow the instructions to put each of the numbers, written at the bottom, in one of the boxes A or B.

Which numbers go into Box A?  Which go into Box B?

4. These lists give the multiples of 4 and the multiples of 5.

   > **Multiples of 4:** 4, 8, 12, 16, 20, 24, 28, 32, 36, 40, 44, . . .
   > **Multiples of 5:** 5, 10, 15, 20, 25, 30, 35, 40, 45, 50, . . .

   (a) What is the smallest number that is a multiple of both 4 and 5?

   (b) Write down two numbers that are multiples of both 4 and 5.

   (c) Continue the lists given above so you can find the first 3 multiples that are common to both 4 and 5.

**Review**

| 1 | 2 | 3 | 4 | 5 | 6 | 7 | 8 | 9 | 10 | 11 | 12 | 13 | 14 | 15 |
|---|---|---|---|---|---|---|---|---|----|----|----|----|----|----|
| 16 | 17 | 18 | 19 | 20 | 21 | 22 | 23 | 24 | 25 | 26 | 27 | 28 | 29 | 30 |

From this list of numbers, write down

(a) the multiples of 2    (b) the multiples of 5 that are greater than 10.

## INVESTIGATION 8:16

**LAST DIGITS**

The multiples of 2 are:  2, 4, 6, 8, 10, 12, 14, 16, 18, 20, 22, 24, 26, 28, 30, . . .
The last digits of these numbers are:  2, 4, 6, 8, 0, 2, 4, 6, 8, 0, 2, 4, 6, 8, 0, . . .
The pattern 2, 4, 6, 8, 0 repeats.

The multiples of 3 are:  3, 6, 9, 12, 15, 18, 21, 24, 27, 30, 33, 36, 39, 42, . . .
The last digits of these numbers are:  3, 6, 9, 2, 5, 8, 1, 4, 7, 0, 3, 6, 9, 2, . . .

Is there a pattern here that repeats? **Investigate.**

**What if** we wrote down the multiples of 4?
**What if** . . .

## INVESTIGATION 8:17

### MORE MULTIPLICATION TABLE PATTERNS

| ×  | 1  | 2  | 3  | 4  | 5  | 6  | 7  | 8  | 9  | 10  |
|----|----|----|----|----|----|----|----|----|----|-----|
| 1  | 1  | 2  | 3  | 4  | 5  | 6  | 7  | 8  | 9  | 10  |
| 2  | 2  | 4  | 6  | 8  | 10 | 12 | 14 | 16 | 18 | 20  |
| 3  | 3  | 6  | 9  | 12 | 15 | 18 | 21 | 24 | 27 | 30  |
| 4  | 4  | 8  | 12 | 16 | 20 | 24 | 28 | 32 | 36 | 40  |
| 5  | 5  | 10 | 15 | 20 | 25 | 30 | 35 | 40 | 45 | 50  |
| 6  | 6  | 12 | 18 | 24 | 30 | 36 | 42 | 48 | 54 | 60  |
| 7  | 7  | 14 | 21 | 28 | 35 | 42 | 49 | 56 | 63 | 70  |
| 8  | 8  | 16 | 24 | 32 | 40 | 48 | 56 | 64 | 72 | 80  |
| 9  | 9  | 18 | 27 | 36 | 45 | 54 | 63 | 72 | 81 | 90  |
| 10 | 10 | 20 | 30 | 40 | 50 | 60 | 70 | 80 | 90 | 100 |

The numbers in the first six rows, which are multiples of 4, are shown in red.

Can you use the pattern to predict which numbers in the other rows are multiples of 4? **Investigate.**

Write out another 10 × 10 multiplication table.

**Investigate** the pattern made when the multiples of 3 are coloured.

**What if** the multiples of 6 are coloured?

**What if** the multiples of 8 are coloured?

**What if** the multiples of 9 are coloured?

The computer can be used to give lists of multiples.

*Example*  A program to calculate and print the first six multiples of 4 could be:

    10  FOR NUMBER = 1 TO 6
    20  PRINT 4 * NUMBER
    30  NEXT NUMBER
    40  END

## PRACTICAL EXERCISE 8:18

Write a program to calculate and print the first 100 multiples of 3 or 5 or 4 or some other number.

Run your program on the computer.

## PUZZLES 8:19

1. I am even.
   I am less than 30.
   I am greater than 20.
   I am a multiple of 3.
   What number am I?

2. I am a multiple of 6.
   I am also a multiple of 4.
   The sum of my digits is a prime number.
   What number am I?

3. Find ten different whole numbers from 1 to 20 so that none of the numbers is a multiple of any of the others.

# FACTORS

A **factor** of a given number is a whole number that divides exactly into the given number.

*Worked Example*  Find all the factors of 12.

*Answer*  Since 12 is divisible by 1, 2, 3, 4, 6 and 12 then the factors of 12 are 1, 2, 3, 4, 6 and 12.

A **prime factor** is a factor that is a prime number.

*Example*  The factors of 12 are 1, 2, 3, 4, 6 and 12.
Of these factors, only 2 and 3 are prime numbers.
The prime factors of 12 are 2 and 3.

## DISCUSSION EXERCISE 8:20

* Tina drew the following diagrams to find the factors of 12. **Discuss** Tina's method.

* What diagrams could you draw to find the factors of 20? **Discuss.**
  **What if** you were asked to find the factors of 10?
  **What if** you were asked to find the factors of 15?
  **What if** . . .

* Brett used this "factor tree" to find the prime factors of 84. Brett claimed that the prime factors were 2, 3 and 7. Was Brett correct? **Discuss** Brett's method.

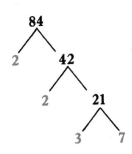

## EXERCISE 8:21

1.  Give all the factors of these numbers.

    (a) 6    (b) 8    (c) 10    (d) 13    (e) 15    (f) 28    (g) 30

    (h) 4    (i) 14    (j) 24

2.  These lists give the factors of 6 and the factors of 15.

    | Factors of 6: 1, 2, 3, 6 | Factors of 15: 1, 3, 5, 15 |
    | --- | --- |

    (a) What two factors are common to both 6 and 15?

    (b) What is the largest common factor of 6 and 15?

3.  (a) List the factors of 12.

    (b) List the factors of 28.

    (c) What factors are common to both 12 and 28?

    (d) What is the largest common factor of both 12 and 28?

4.  Find the common factors of

    (a) 18 and 24          (b) 16 and 36          (c) 40 and 25

    (d) 6 and 18           (e) 20 and 36          (f) 32 and 80

    (g) 18 and 63          (h) 11 and 17.

5.  Find the missing numbers A, B, C on these factor trees.

    (a)                    (b)                    (c)

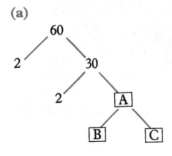
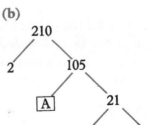
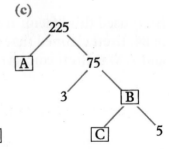

6. Write down all the prime factors (i.e. the factors that are prime numbers) of these.

   (a) 2     (b) 6     (c) 7     (d) 12     (e) 16     (f) 19     (g) 25

   (h) 36     (i) 8     (j) 18

7. **Start**

| 25 | 50 | 33 | 10 | 4 | 6 | 27 |
|----|----|----|----|----|----|----|
| 21 | 28 | 15 | 35 | 63 | 14 | 15 |
| 6 | 39 | 26 | 12 | 35 | 9 | 40 |
| 45 | 4 | 3 | 15 | 42 | 55 | 35 |
| 9 | 8 | 33 | 38 | 11 | 77 | 14 |
| 12 | 36 | 35 | 66 | 99 | 51 | 75 |

**Finish**

Starting at 25 make your way down to 75. Move one square at a time through numbers which have a common factor greater than 1. You may move sideways or up or down but not diagonally. Write down the numbers you pass through.

**Review 1**  (a) Write down all the factors of 48.

(b) Write down the prime factors of 140.

(c) Find the common factors of 14 and 35.

(d) What is the largest common factor of 16 and 40?

**Review 2**

A bagpipe has the same number of pipes as the number of factors of 16. How many pipes are in a bagpipe?

**Review 3**

| 2 | 3 | 4 | 5 | 6 | 7 | 9 | 12 | 15 | 21 | 25 | 28 | 35 | 36 |
|---|---|---|---|---|---|---|----|----|----|----|----|----|----|

Copy this list of numbers.         Cross out the factors of 36.

Cross out the multiples of 7.         Cross out the factors of 30.

Which number is left?

## GAME 8:22

**FACTOR FUN: a game for two players (A and B).**

Copy this number square.

| 1 | 2 | 3 | 4 | 5 | 6 |
|---|---|---|---|---|---|
| 7 | 8 | 9 | 10 | 11 | 12 |
| 13 | 14 | 15 | 16 | 17 | 18 |
| 19 | 20 | 21 | 22 | 23 | 24 |
| 25 | 26 | 27 | 28 | 29 | 30 |
| 31 | 32 | 33 | 34 | 35 | 36 |

Toss a coin to see who goes first. If A wins the toss, A crosses out any number. This number is A's score.

B then crosses out as many factors of this number as he or she can find and adds them. This is B's score.

B then crosses out a number that is still left and adds this to his or her score. A then crosses out as many factors of this number as he or she can find and adds these to his or her score. Then A crosses out a number that is still left and adds this to his or her score.

The game continues in this way until all the numbers have been crossed out. The winner is the one with the highest score.

For instance, if A crosses out 28 the game starts as shown.

| 1 | 2 | 3 | 4 | 5 | 6 |
|---|---|---|---|---|---|
| 7 | 8 | 9 | 10 | 11 | 12 |
| 13 | 14 | 15 | 16 | 17 | 18 |
| 19 | 20 | 21 | 22 | 23 | 24 |
| 25 | 26 | 27 | 28 | 29 | 30 |
| 31 | 32 | 33 | 34 | 35 | 36 |

A crosses out 28.
A's score = 28.

| 1 | 2 | 3 | 4 | 5 | 6 |
|---|---|---|---|---|---|
| 7 | 8 | 9 | 10 | 11 | 12 |
| 13 | 14 | 15 | 16 | 17 | 18 |
| 19 | 20 | 21 | 22 | 23 | 24 |
| 25 | 26 | 27 | 28 | 29 | 30 |
| 31 | 32 | 33 | 34 | 35 | 36 |

B crosses out 1, 2, 4, 7, 14.
B's score = 1 + 2 + 4 + 7 + 14
= 28

| 1 | 2 | 3 | 4 | 5 | 6 |
|---|---|---|---|---|---|
| 7 | 8 | 9 | 10 | 11 | 12 |
| 13 | 14 | 15 | 16 | 17 | 18 |
| 19 | 20 | 21 | 22 | 23 | 24 |
| 25 | 26 | 27 | 28 | 29 | 30 |
| 31 | 32 | 33 | 34 | 35 | 36 |

B crosses out 32.
B's score = 28 + 32
= 60

A crosses out 8, 16.
A's score = 28 + 8 + 16
= 52

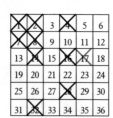

A crosses out 17.
A's score = 52 + 17
= 69

B cannot cross out any factors of 17.
B crosses out 35.
B's score is now 95.
It is now A's turn.

## PUZZLES 8:23

?? ? ? ? ? ? ? ? ? ? ? ? ? ? ? ? ? ? ? ? ? ? ? ? ? ? ? ? ? ? ? ? ? ? ? ? ? ? ? ? ? ? ? ? ? ? ??

1. I am a prime number.
   I am a factor of 21.
   I am not a factor of 12.
   What number am I?

2. I am a factor of 30 and also of 48.
   I am not a factor of 15 or of 16.
   What number am I?

3. A 30 year old mother has two children at school. The age of each child is a factor of the mother's age. The sum of their ages is also a factor of the mother's age. How old are the children?

4. What is the smallest number that has exactly 5 factors?

5. What number under 100 has the largest number of factors? Is there more than one answer?

?? ? ? ? ? ? ? ? ? ? ? ? ? ? ? ? ? ? ? ? ? ? ? ? ? ? ? ? ? ? ? ? ? ? ? ? ? ? ? ? ? ? ? ? ? ??

## SQUARE NUMBERS

When a number is multiplied by itself, the answer is called a **square number**.

For instance, since $7 \times 7 = 49$, 49 is a square number.

## EXERCISE 8:24

1. Write down all the two-digit square numbers.

**2.**

| 1 | 2 | 4 | 5 | 12 | 13 | 16 | 17 | 19 | 21 | 26 | 32 | 39 | 42 | 49 |

(a) Copy this list of numbers.

(b) Cross out the square numbers.

(c) Cross out the even numbers between 25 and 35.

(d) Cross out the factors of 25.

(e) Cross out the odd numbers between 10 and 20.

(f) Cross out the multiples of 3.

(g) Which number is left?

**3.** What is the next number?

(a) 1, 4, 9, ...

(b) 3, 6, 9, ...

(c) 5, 10, 15, ...

(d) 8, 12, 16, ...

(e) 18, 24, 30, ...

(f) 9, 16, 25, ...

**Review**  Copy this diagram.

Shade all the parts with

(a) factors of 15

(b) square numbers

(c) multiples of 9.

Which part is not shaded?

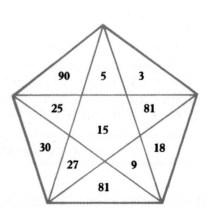

## PUZZLE 8:25

?????????????????????????????????????????????
> I have two digits.
> One of my factors is 3.
> I am not a multiple of 8.
> I am an even number.
> I am a square number.
>
> What number am I?

?????????????????????????????????????????????

### JUST FOR FUN

1. **Step 1**   Write down any three-digit number.

   **Step 2**   Write this number down again to make a six-digit number.

   **Step 3**   Divide by 77.

   **Step 4**   Divide by 13.

   What do you notice about your answer?

2. **Step 1**   Write down a two-digit number.

   **Step 2**   Multiply one of the digits by 5, add 6 to the answer and double the result.

   **Step 3**   Add on the other digit, then subtract 12.

   What do you notice about your answer?

3. **Step 1**   Write down any multiple of 9 that is less than 91.

   **Step 2**   Add a number between 1 and 9.

   **Step 3**   Add together the digits of the number you now have.
   If this total is a two-digit number keep on adding the digits until you get a one-digit number.

   What do you notice about your answer?

**DID YOU KNOW** that a formula gives the relationship between two or more things?

---

## DISCUSSION EXERCISE 9:1

• Suppose a take-away meal costs £3.

What is the cost of 1 meal?
What is the cost of 2 meals?
What is the cost of 3 meals?

Suppose in one day many of these meals were bought. How could the total cost be worked out?
What is the relationship between the total cost and the number of meals bought?

**Discuss** with your group.

• 1cm = 10mm

How many mm in 5cm? How many mm in 8cm? How many mm in 20cm?

Suppose a length was measured in cm. How could the length then be written down in mm?
What is the relationship between the length in cm and the length in mm?

**Discuss** with your group.

 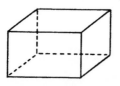 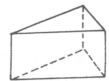 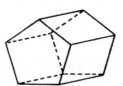 

A relationship between the edges, faces and vertices of a solid shape is "the number of edges is two less than the sum of the number of faces and vertices." (Remember that a face is a flat surface, an edge is a line where two faces meet and a vertex is a corner.)

Test this relationship on the solid shapes drawn above.

## USING FORMULAE

*Worked Example*

A formula for the number of matchsticks needed to make any of the matchstick houses in this pattern is "multiply the number of houses by four, then add one."

Use this formula to find the number of matchsticks needed for the diagram that has  (a) 5 houses
(b) 24 houses.

*Answer*   (a) $5 \times 4 = 20$;   $20 + 1 = 21$.
Number of matchsticks needed = 21.

(b) $24 \times 4 = 96$;   $96 + 1 = 97$.
Number of matchsticks needed = 97.

*Worked Example*  When the Gaelic Singers went on tour in Canada they stayed in motels. The formula for the cost of these motels is "£35 for one person plus £12 for each extra person."

Find the cost of a motel in which   (a) 4 people stayed

(b) 5 people stayed.

*Answer*   (a) Cost for one person = £35

Cost for the 3 extra = $3 \times £12$
$= £36$

Total cost for the 4 people $= £35 + £36$
$= £71$

(b) Cost for one person = £35

Cost for the 4 extra = $4 \times £12$
$= £48$

Total cost for the 5 people $= £35 + £48$
$= £83$

## EXERCISE 9:2

1.

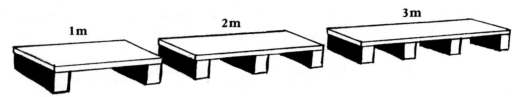

Shelves are made from a length of timber and bricks. The length (in metres) of the shelf is given by "one less than the number of bricks."

Use this formula to find the length of the shelf that is on

    (a) 5 bricks

    (b) 9 bricks

    (c) 16 bricks

    (d) 30 bricks.

2.

In this fence there are 10 posts and 45 spacers.

A formula that gives the relationship between the number of spacers and the number of posts is "multiply the number of posts by 5, then subtract 5 to get the number of spacers."

Use this formula to find the number of spacers needed to build a fence with

    (a) 6 posts

    (b) 9 posts

    (c) 25 posts

    (d) 50 posts.

3.

A formula that gives the relationship between the number of black and red dots is "add two to double the number of red dots to get the number of black dots."

Use this formula to find the number of black dots in a diagram which has

    (a) 5 red dots   12

    (b) 8 red dots   18

    (c) 35 red dots   72

    (d) 105 red dots.   212.

4.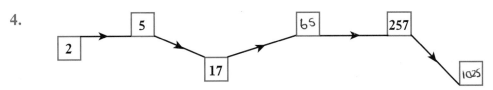

A formula that gives the relationship between each number and the following number is "subtract 3 from 4 times the number."

Use this formula to find the missing numbers.

5. A recipe for cooking lamb gives the cooking time as "40 min per kg plus 20 min more."

What is the cooking time for a piece of lamb that weighs

  (a) 2kg        (b) 3kg        (c) 4kg        (d) 0·5kg?

6. Advertisements in a magazine cost £10 plus £4 for each line.

How much does it cost for an advertisement of

  (a) 4 lines

  (b) 8 lines

  (c) 18 lines?

7. A formula for finding the perimeter of a rectangle is "add the length and the width, then double this answer."

   Use this formula to find the perimeter of a rectangle if

   (a) length = 7cm, width = 5cm

   (b) length = 14cm, width = 10cm

   (c) length = 78mm, width = 42mm

   (d) length = 1·2m, width = 0·9m.

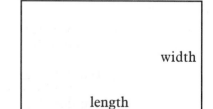

8. To change a temperature given in °C to °F we can use the formula "multiply by 9, then divide by 5, then add 32." Use this formula to change the following to °F.

   (a) 100°C     (b) 0°C     (c) 50 °C     (d) 30°C     (e) 10°C

## Review 1

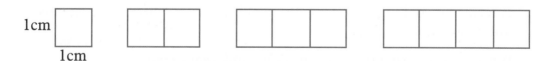

1cm

1cm

A formula for the perimeter (in cm) of each of the diagrams in this pattern is "two more than twice the number of squares".

Use this formula to find the perimeter of a pattern which has

    (a) 5 squares

    (b) 10 squares

    (c) 20 squares

    (d) 100 squares.

**Review 2**   A formula for changing kilograms to pounds is "multiply by 11, then divide by 5."

Use this formula to answer the following.

(a) Lin weighs 50kg. In pounds, how heavy is Lin?

(b) Lin's dog weighs 30kg. How heavy is this dog, in pounds?

**Review 3**   A formula for finding the area of a rectangle is "multiply the length by the width."

Use this formula to find the area of a rectangle if

(a) length = 5, width = 4      (b) length = 7, width = 3

(c) length = 18, width = 8.

## PRACTICAL EXERCISE 9:3

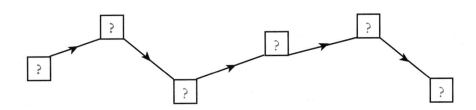

Write down a formula such as "double each number and subtract five to find the next number."

Use your formula to make a number chain.

Give your number chain to other members of your group. Ask them to find the relationship between each number and the next number.

Your group could make many number chains and ask another group to find the relationships.

## PUZZLE 9:4

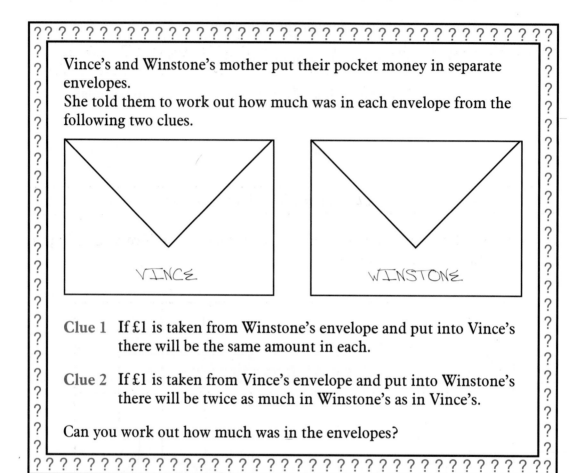

Vince's and Winstone's mother put their pocket money in separate envelopes.
She told them to work out how much was in each envelope from the following two clues.

**Clue 1**  If £1 is taken from Winstone's envelope and put into Vince's there will be the same amount in each.

**Clue 2**  If £1 is taken from Vince's envelope and put into Winstone's there will be twice as much in Winstone's as in Vince's.

Can you work out how much was in the envelopes?

## JUST FOR FUN

*Step 1*   Write down a number.

*Step 2*   Multiply by 3.

*Step 3*   Add 6.

*Step 4*   Divide by 3.

*Step 5*   Subtract the number you wrote down at Step 1.

Repeat *Steps 1 to 5* with another number.
What do you notice about your answers?

**DID YOU KNOW**    that in the 17th century René Descartes, a Frenchman, thought of the idea of using two numbers to explain the position of an object?

## DISCUSSION EXERCISE 10:1

One story which is told is that René Descartes thought of his idea while lying in bed looking at a fly on the ceiling.

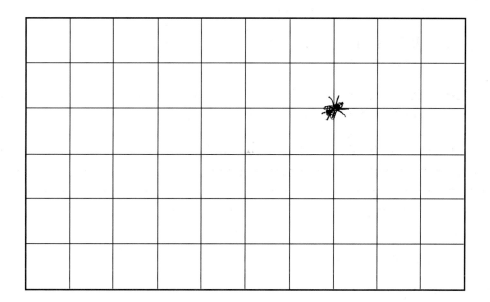

René Descartes imagined a grid of lines drawn across the ceiling.

**Discuss** how the position of the fly might then be described using two numbers.

Did you begin counting at one of the corners? If you did, does it matter which corner? **Discuss.**

# COORDINATES

A way of describing the position of a point is by using two numbered lines, called axes. These are the lines labelled x and y on the diagram.

The horizontal axis is called the x-axis.

The vertical axis is called the y-axis.

The point where the two axes meet is called the origin. (Note: axes is the plural of axis.)

The numbers on the axes are written on the lines, not in the spaces between the lines.

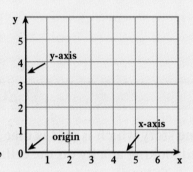

The position of a point is described using a number on the x-axis and a number on the y-axis.

To plot a point on a graph:     **begin at the origin**
    **first move along**
    **then move up**

For instance, the dotted lines show how we plot the point A(3, 2). We begin at the origin, then move along 3, then move up 2.

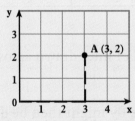

A(3, 2).     3 is the x-coordinate. This is the distance we go along.
    2 is the y-coordinate. This is the distance we go up.

## GAME 10:2

**TARGET PRACTICE: a game for a group.**

**Equipment:** 2 dice, one red and the other white.
A graph, drawn up as shown, for each player.

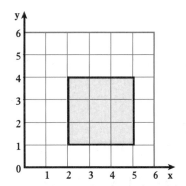

**The Play:** The players take turns to throw both dice.
The number on the red die is the x-coordinate; the number on the white die is the y-coordinate.

A dot is placed on a player's graph at the point given by the numbers on the dice. A dot that is on the target (the grey square) is a "hit".
The first player to score 5 hits is the winner.

Variation: Draw a target of a different shape.

## EXERCISE 10:3

1.

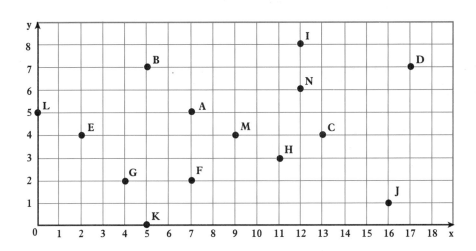

Write down the coordinates of each of the points A, B, C, . . . , N.

2.  On graph paper, draw x and y-axes.
    Number the x-axis from 0 to 15. Number the y-axis from 0 to 6.

    Plot these points on your graph.   A(2, 5)   B(5, 2)   C(6, 4)   D(4, 6)   E(0, 3)

    F(3, 0)   G(11, 1)   H(4, 4)   I(12, 5)   J(0, 6)   K(6, 0)   V(8, 3)   W(14, 6)

3.  On graph paper, draw x and y-axes.
    Number the x-axis up to 20. Number the y-axis up to 5.

    (a) Plot the following points.
        Join each point to the next point with a straight line.

        (4, 5)   (4, 3)   (6, 5)   (9, 5)   (11, 4)   (12, 3)   (12, 1)   (20, 1)   (0, 1)

        (2, 3)   (2, 4)   (3, 5)   (4, 5)

        Now place a large dot at (2, 2).

    (b) What have you drawn?

4.

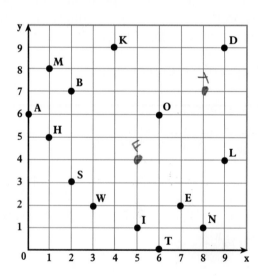

Write down the letter that is beside each of the following points.
You should end up with a sentence.
What does the sentence say?

(6, 6) (8, 1) (7, 2)          (1, 8) (5, 1) (2, 3) (6, 0) (0, 6) (4, 9) (7, 2)

(0, 6) (8, 1) (9, 9)          (6, 0) (1, 5) (5, 1) (2, 3)

(3, 2) (5, 1) (9, 4) (9, 4)          (2, 7) (7, 2)

(8, 1) (6, 6) (8, 1) (2, 3) (7, 2) (8, 1) (2, 3) (7, 2)

5.

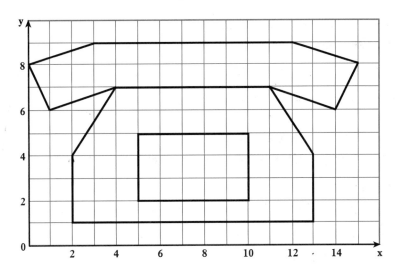

The instructions to draw this shape could be:

*Plot these points and join them in order.*

(a) *(5, 2)  (5, 5)  (10, 5)  (10, 2)  (5, 2)*

(b) *(11, 7)  (4, 7)  (1, 6) ...*

Finish the instructions in **(b)**.

**Review 1**   On graph paper, draw x and y-axes.
Number both axes from 0 to 11.

(a) Plot the following points.
Join each point to the next point with a straight line.

(2, 2)  (2, 10)  (10, 10)  (10, 2)  (4, 2)  (4, 8)  (8, 8)

(8, 4)  (6, 4)  (6, 6)

(b) Describe the shape you have made.

**Review 2**   The instructions to draw this
shape could begin:

*Join these points in order:*
*(4, 1) (5, 2) ...*

Finish these instructions.

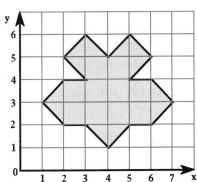

137

## INVESTIGATION 10:4

### COORDINATE PICTURES

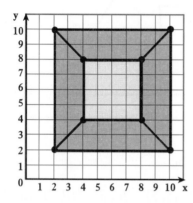 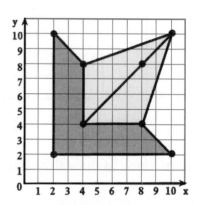

These two "pictures" were made by joining the dots at (2, 2)  (2, 10)
(10, 2)  (10, 10)  (4, 4)  (4, 8)  (8, 4)  (8, 8) with lines.

What other "pictures" could be made by joining these points in different
ways? **Investigate.**

## PRACTICAL EXERCISE 10:5

1.  On a set of axes, draw a picture made by joining dots with straight lines.

    Using coordinates, write instructions for drawing this picture.

    Give your instructions to other members of your group or class. Ask them to
    draw the picture from your instructions.

2.  Choose an object in the classroom or in the school grounds.

    On a set of axes, draw an outline of this object using straight lines. Have each
    corner of your object where two grid lines meet.

    Using coordinates, write instructions for drawing this object.

    Give your instructions to another member of your class or group. Ask them
    to name your object.

## GAME 10:6

**SINK THE SHIPS: a game for 2 players.**

Equipment:    A graph for each player. The numbers on each axis from 0 to 10.

Preparation:  Each player secretly puts the following ships on his or her graph.

1 submarine (1 dot)
2 destroyers (2 dots each)
1 cruiser (3 dots)
1 battleship (4 dots)

An example is shown.

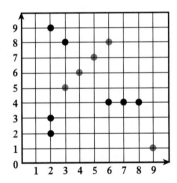

The Play:    The players take it in turn to name a coordinate.

If one of the opponent's dots is at this coordinate the opponent says "hit"; otherwise the opponent says "miss". The opponent puts a cross through a dot that has been hit. Once all the dots belonging to a ship have been hit, the opponent must say "ship sunk".

The loser is the first player to have all of his or her ships sunk.

# INVESTIGATION 10:7

## ESCAPE ROUTE

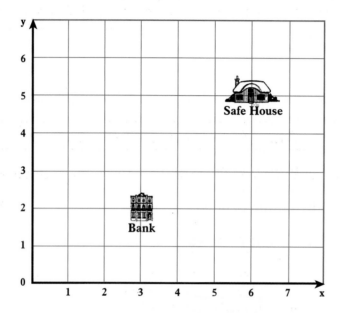

The police are called while robbers are robbing a bank at (3, 2). The robbers have a get-away car.

The police have 3 cars trying to stop the robbers getting from the bank to their safe house at (6, 5).
The police cars can travel at the same speed as the get-away car.
The police cars can telephone each other and the bank.
The police do not have time to place their cars closer than one block from the bank. (One square on the graph represents one block.)

Can the police place their 3 cars so that the robbers cannot get back to their safe house? **Investigate.**

**What if** the police do not have time to place their cars closer than two blocks from the bank?

**What if** the police had 4 cars?
**What if** the police had 5 cars?
**What if** ...

## COORDINATES on the COMPUTER

On a computer screen, one square is very small.

A line drawn between the points (2, 3) and (5, 12) would be very small indeed.
A line drawn between the points (200, 300) and (500, 1200) would be able to be
seen clearly.

## PRACTICAL EXERCISE 10:8

This BASIC program draws a double-headed arrow within a rectangle.

```
10    MODE   4
20    MOVE   0, 0
30    DRAW   1250, 0
40    DRAW   1250, 1000
50    DRAW   0, 1000
60    DRAW   0, 0
70    MOVE   150, 500
80    DRAW   350, 200
90    DRAW   350, 300
100   DRAW   900, 300
110   DRAW   900, 200
120   DRAW   1100, 500
130   DRAW   900, 800
140   DRAW   900, 700
150   DRAW   350, 700
160   DRAW   350, 800
170   DRAW   150, 300
180   END
```

Draw this shape using this program.

Write programs to draw other shapes.
Use your programs to draw the shapes.

## INVESTIGATION 10:9

### COMPUTER NAMES

# TINA ROB

Which of these names could be drawn accurately on the computer?
How could you draw a good approximation for the name that cannot be
drawn accurately?
Investigate.

### PROJECT

- Make up a game which uses coordinates.

  You may like to change one of the games in this chapter. You may like
  to make up quite a different sort of game.

- Plan a new layout for your maths. classroom using coordinates.

  You may prefer to plan a layout for another room in your school.

  You may like to use the computer in this project.

1. Write down the letter that is beside each of the following points. You should end up with a sentence. What does this sentence say?

    (2, 0)  (4, 5)  (2, 4)  (0, 2)

    (2, 4)  (5, 7)  (5, 4)  (7, 6)

    (2, 6)  (4, 2)

    (7, 5)  (7, 6)  (7, 6)  (6, 2)  (7, 6)  (6, 2)

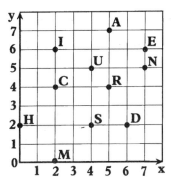

2. | 32355 | 35532 | 35320 | 33204 | 33024 | 34380 | 32550 |

    One of these numbers is divisible by 3, 4 and 5. Which one?

3. Copy and finish these.
    Use the patterns to find the numbers that go in the boxes.

    (a)       $3 \times 5 =$      (b)      $2222 \div 22 =$      (c)      $1 \times 9 =$

    $33 \times 5 =$          $22422 \div 222 =$        $21 \times 9 =$

    $333 \times 5 =$        $224422 \div 2222 =$       $321 \times 9 =$

    $3333 \times 5 =$      $2244422 \div 22222 =$      $4321 \times 9 =$

                                                    $54321 \times 9 =$

    $33333333 \times 5 = \square$       $\square \div 222222 = 101$

                                                      $87654321 \times 9 = \square$

4. When Matthew buys sausages for a barbecue, he buys 2 for each person plus 5 extra.

    How many sausages does Matthew buy for

          (a) 12 people

          (b) 20 people

          (c) 25 people?

5.

| × | 1 | 2 | 3 | 4 | 5 | 6 | 7 | 8 | 9 | 10 |
|---|---|---|---|---|---|---|---|---|---|---|
| 1 | 1 | 2 | 3 | 4 | 5 | 6 | 7 | 8 | 9 | 10 |
| 2 | 2 | 4 | 6 | 8 | 10 | 12 | 14 | 16 | 18 | 20 |
| 3 | 3 | 6 | 9 | 12 | 15 | 18 | 21 | 24 | 27 | 30 |
| 4 | 4 | 8 | 12 | 16 | 20 | 24 | 28 | 32 | 36 | 40 |
| 5 | 5 | 10 | 15 | 20 | 25 | 30 | 35 | 40 | 45 | 50 |
| 6 | 6 | 12 | 18 | 24 | 30 | 36 | 42 | 48 | 54 | 60 |
| 7 | 7 | 14 | 21 | 28 | 35 | 42 | 49 | 56 | 63 | 70 |
| 8 | 8 | 16 | 24 | 32 | 40 | 48 | 56 | 64 | 72 | 80 |
| 9 | 9 | 18 | 27 | 36 | 45 | 54 | 63 | 72 | 81 | 90 |
| 10 | 10 | 20 | 30 | 40 | 50 | 60 | 70 | 80 | 90 | 100 |

The numbers in red are the numbers in the first 6 rows that are divisible by 3.

Can you use the pattern to predict which numbers in the other rows are divisible by 3?

6.  
I am a prime number.  
I am a factor of 30.  
I am not a factor of 24.  
What number am I?

7.

A formula for the number of matchsticks needed to make any diagram in this pattern is "one more than three times the number of squares."

Use this formula to find the number of matchsticks needed for the diagram that has

(a) 4 squares

(b) 14 squares

(c) 34 squares

(d) 94 squares.

8.

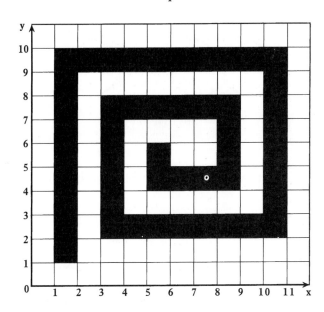

The instructions to draw this shape could be:

*Join these points in order:* *(10, 9)* *(2, 9)* *(2, 1)* . . .

Finish these instructions.

9. Efra and Sarah both played in a cricket match.
   Efra said that the number of runs she made could be worked out as follows:
   "Multiply Sarah's runs by 3, then subtract 14."

   If Sarah made 21 runs, how many did Efra make?

10. Copy this grid of numbers.

   Shade the squares with factors of 24.
   Shade the squares with multiples of 5.
   Shade the squares with multiples of 3.
   Shade the squares with factors of 28.

   Which square is not shaded?

| 48 | 5 | 4 | 12 | 18 |
|----|----|----|----|----|
| 8 | 7 | 40 | 72 | 4 |
| 3 | 15 | 21 | 1 | 60 |
| 65 | 11 | 24 | 27 | 6 |
| 9 | 30 | 2 | 20 | 28 |

11.

 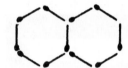 

(a) Draw the next diagram in this pattern of matchstick hexagons.

(b) How many hexagons will be in the ninth diagram?

(c) How many matchsticks will be used for the ninth diagram?

12. A formula for changing miles to kilometres is "multiply by 8, then divide by 5."
Use this formula to answer the following.

(a) Maryanne is training for a marathon.
Each morning she runs 15 miles.
How far is this in kilometres?

(b) Andrew travels 16 miles to work.
In kilometres, how far does Andrew travel?

13. One factor of 36 is 36. The sum of the digits of this factor is a square number.

(a) Write down all the factors of 36.

(b) Which other factor has digits which add to a square number?

(c) Which factors of 36 are square numbers?

(d) Which factors of 36 are prime numbers?

14.

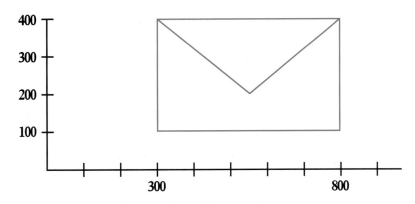

Finish the BASIC program to draw this shape.

```
10   MODE  4
20   MOVE  300, 100
30   DRAW  300, 400
40   DRAW  550, 200
     .
     .
     .
```

# SHAPE, SPACE and MEASURES

# Shape, Space and Measures from Previous Levels

**2-D SHAPES**

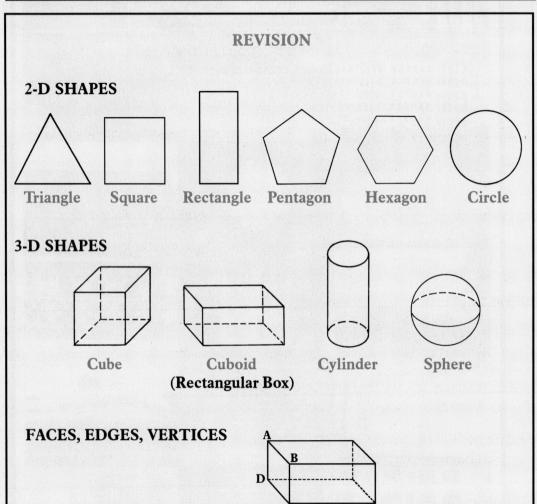

Triangle   Square   Rectangle   Pentagon   Hexagon   Circle

**3-D SHAPES**

Cube   Cuboid   Cylinder   Sphere
**(Rectangular Box)**

**FACES, EDGES, VERTICES**

A face is a flat surface.
For instance, the above shape has 6 faces; a top face, a bottom face, a front face, a back face, and two side faces. One of the side faces is ABCD.

An edge is a line where two faces meet.
For instance, the above shape has 12 edges. Four of these are AB, DC, AD, BC.

A vertex is a corner where edges meet. (**Vertices** is the plural of vertex.)
For instance, the above shape has 8 vertices. Four of these are A, B, C, D.

*continued . . .*

*. . . from previous page*

# SYMMETRY

A shape has **reflective symmetry** if it can be folded so that one half fits exactly onto the other half.

For instance:  This shape is symmetrical about the dotted line.
The dotted line is called a **line of symmetry.**

For instance: 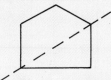 This shape is not symmetrical about the dotted line.

For instance:  This shape is symmetrical about the shaded plane.
The shaded plane is called a **plane of symmetry.**

# ANGLE

**Angle** is a measure of turn.

A **right angle** is a quarter of a complete turn.
For instance, if we turn from facing North to facing East we turn through a right angle.

The symbol for a right angle is a small square written in the angle, as shown here.

# MOVEMENTS

 This arrow shows a movement in a clockwise direction.
**Clockwise** is the direction in which the hands of a clock move.

 This arrow shows a movement in an anticlockwise direction.
**Anticlockwise** is the opposite direction to that in which the hands of a clock move.

*continued . . .*

*. . . from previous page*

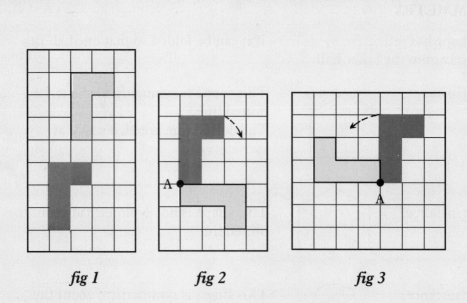

fig 1                    fig 2                    fig 3

*fig 1* shows a **translation** (or **straight movement**). The red shape has been translated 1 square to the right and 4 squares up to the shaded shape.

*fig 2* and *fig 3* show **rotation** (or **turning movement**).

In *fig 2* the red shape has been rotated clockwise about A, through $\frac{1}{4}$ turn or 1 right angle.

In *fig 3* the red shape has been rotated anticlockwise about A, through $\frac{1}{4}$ turn.

## MEASURES

Commonly used **units** are:  **Money** — pound (£), pence (p)

**Time** — hour (h), minute (min), second (sec)

**Length** — kilometre (km), metre (m), centimetre (cm), millimetre (mm)

**Capacity** — litre (*l* or L), millilitre (m*l* or mL)

**Mass** — kilogram (kg), gram (g)

## REVISION EXERCISE

1.  Name these shapes.

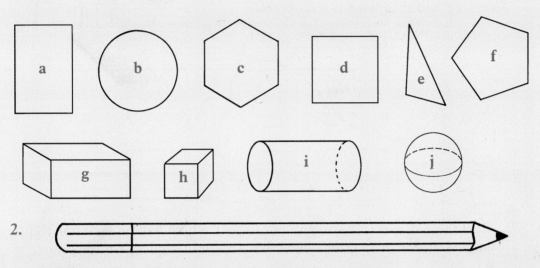

2.

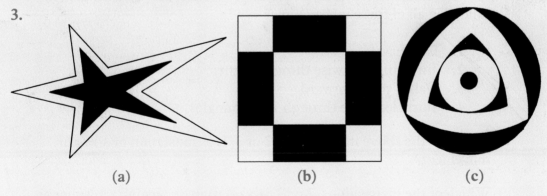

(a) To the nearest centimetre, how long is this pencil?

(b) To the nearest millimetre, how long is this pencil?

3.

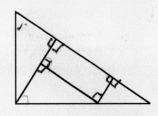

(a)          (b)          (c)

How many lines of symmetry do these shapes have?

4.  How many right angles are there in this shape?

5. Victoria needs pieces of wood, each 3 metres long, for the bookshelf she is making.
She cuts some of these from an 8 metre plank.

What length of this plank is left over?

6.

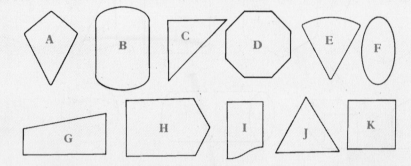

(a) Sort these shapes into two groups: a group which have at least one right-angled corner and a group which have no right-angled corners.

(b) Sort these shapes in other ways.
Explain how you decided which group each shape was in.

7. (a) In which direction (North, South, East or West) are you facing after following all of these instructions?

    1. Face East.
    2. Turn anticlockwise through $\frac{1}{4}$ turn.
    3. Walk 5 paces forward.
    4. Turn clockwise through 2 right angles.

(b) Which of the above instructions, 2 or 3, is a translation or straight movement?

(c) Which of the instructions, 2 or 3, is a rotation or turning movement?

8. These diagrams show two of the planes of syr

Draw a cube. (You could trace one of these.)
Shade another plane of symmetry.

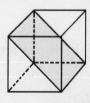
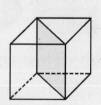

9. (a) Draw a shape with 6 sides and 3 right-angled corners.

   (b) Draw some other shapes.
   Describe your shapes using words such as: square corners, curved edges, equal sides etc.

10. The time on clock (a) is ten past three. What is the time on the other clocks?

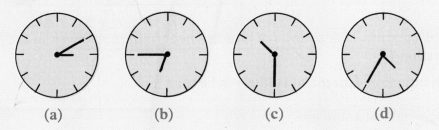

       (a)            (b)           (c)           (d)

11.

| Cube | Cuboid | Cylinder | Sphere |
|------|--------|----------|--------|

Which name in the box describes
   (a) a snooker ball

   (b) a water tank

   (c) a breakfast cereal box

   (d) a die?

12. What reading is given by each of the pointers?

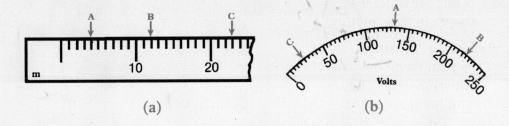

         (a)                     (b)

13.

   (a) How many edges does this shape have?

   (b) How many vertices does this shape have?

   (c) Three of the faces are rectangular.
   How many other faces are there?
   What shape are these?

155

14.

| min | cm | m*l* | kg | m | mm | *l* | g | km | sec |
|-----|-----|------|-----|-----|-----|-----|-----|-----|-----|

The abbreviation for each of the following is given in the box: kilometre, metre, centimetre, millimetre, gram, kilogram, litre, millilitre, minute, second.

Match the words with their abbreviations.

15. For this question, choose units of measurement from those given in the box in **question 14**.

Which unit of measurement is likely to be used for

(a) the weight of a suitcase

(b) the distance from the North Pole to Glasgow

(c) the amount of water in a bath

(d) the time to do 50 additions and subtractions

(e) the height of a school chair

(f) the mass of a paper clip?

16.

(a) Name the different shapes in this "picture".

(b) Make a "picture" of your own. Describe your "picture" and the shapes in it.

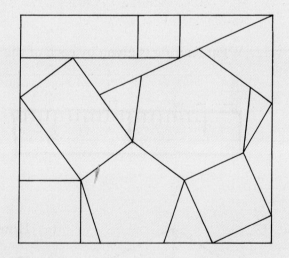

17. A video recorder is set to record a programme that begins at 8·30 p.m. and finishes at 9·45 p.m.

What time will show in the Finish "box"?

| Start | Finish |
|-------|--------|
| **20:30** | **:** |

18.

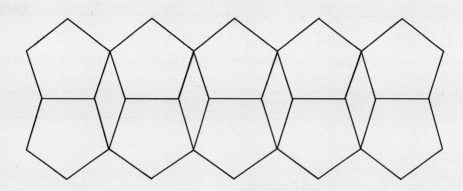

This pattern is made by drawing pentagons.

Make a pattern by drawing hexagons or rectangles or squares or circles.

You may like to use more than one shape in your pattern.

You could colour your pattern.

19.

The LOGO turtle is facing the direction shown.

In which of the following directions will the turtle be facing after the instruction LEFT 90?

A          B          C          D          E

**DID YOU KNOW** that the metre was once defined by:
distance from North Pole to Equator = 10000000 metres

•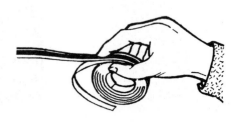

The metre is a metric unit.
What other metric units do you know? **Discuss.**

•

Before we began using metric units we used imperial units. These were also known as British units.

The foot is an imperial unit. What other imperial units do you know?
**Discuss.**

• Write down 3 sports. For instance: cricket, basketball, sailing.
Write down 3 jobs. For instance: nursing, painting, farming.

Make a list of the things that need to be measured in these sports and jobs.
**Discuss.**

**Discuss** which unit of measurement is usually used to measure each thing in your list.

# CHOOSING UNITS for MEASUREMENT

## DISCUSSION EXERCISE 12:2

● Three different weighing instruments are shown.

What units of mass would be written on each of these scales? Name 5 different things you would weigh on each of these. Discuss.

Think of other weighing instruments.
What would be the biggest and smallest mass that could be measured on these? Discuss.

● What can you think of that would be measured in litres?
What can you think of that would be measured in millilitres? Discuss.

● Think of some measuring instruments that are used to measure length.
Which of these could be used to measure a small length such as 6 mm?
Which of these could be used to measure a distance such as 54 km? Discuss.

● The weight of a lorry could be 6 tonnes.
What else might be weighed in tonnes? Discuss.

● What measuring instruments are used to measure time? Discuss.

● Make a list of the things you sometimes measure.
Beside each item, write down the measuring instrument you would use.
Also write down the unit (m, seconds, kg etc.) you would use for the measurement.

## EXERCISE 12:3

1.  Which of these units would the following be measured in?

    | km | m | cm | mm |
    |----|---|----|----|

    (a) the width of a netball court     (b) the length of a motorway

    (c) the width of a postage stamp     (d) the thickness of a paperback book

    (e) the distance between two cities     (f) the height of a cathedral

    (g) the length of a fingernail     (h) the width of a football pitch

    (i) the length of an ant     (j) the thickness of a coin

    (k) the distance to Paris     (1) the length of the Amazon River

2.  Which of these units would the following be measured in?

    | tonne | kg | g | mg |
    |-------|----|----|----|

    The weight of     (a) a lorry     (b) a packet of biscuits

    (c) a feather     (d) an apple

    (e) a dog     (f) a bag of sweets

    (g) a T-bone steak     (h) a ship

3.  Which of these units would the capacity of the following be measured in?

    | l | ml |
    |---|----|

    (a) a bucket     (b) a cup     (c) a fridge

    (d) a washing machine     (e) a spoonful of medicine     (f) a yoghurt pottle

4. Which unit of time (hours, minutes, seconds) would the following be measured in?

   (a) time to count to ten            (b) time to eat an ice-cream

   (c) a flight from Heathrow to Hawaii     (d) time to run 50 metres

   (e) time to do a maths. exercise

5. Which metric unit would probably be used in the Guinness Book of Records for the following?

   (a) the heaviest man

   (b) the shortest time to travel around the world

   (c) the longest length of spaghetti

   (d) the tallest building

   (e) the diameter of the biggest doughnut

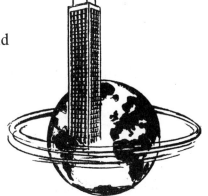

## Review

| t | kg | g | mg | km | m | cm | mm | *l* | m*l* | min | sec |

Which of the units in the box would you measure each of the following in?

(a) length of a building            (b) time to eat dinner

(c) mass of an ant                  (d) amount of tea in a tea bag

(e) thickness of a ruler            (f) diameter of an aspirin

(g) length of a Boeing 747          (h) time to run the length of a cricket pitch

(i) weight of a loaded lorry        (j) distance around the Equator

(k) weight of a bag of potatoes     (l) amount of milk added to a cup of coffee

(m) time for 8 heartbeats           (n) amount of water used in a shower

# USING DECIMALS in MEASUREMENT

We can find a measurement to the nearest tenth or hundredth of a unit by using a scale with many divisions.

There are 10 divisions on this scale.
Each division is $\frac{1}{10}$ m. This is written as 0·1m.
The arrow is pointing to $\frac{4}{10}$ m. This is written as 0·4m.

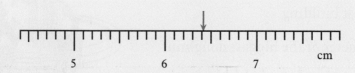

There are 10 divisions between the 6 and the 7.
Each small division is $\frac{1}{10}$ cm; that is 0·1cm.
The arrow is pointing to 4 small divisions after the 6. It is pointing to 6·4cm.

Each large division on this scale is 0·1m or $\frac{1}{10}$ of a metre.
There are 10 small divisions between each large division. Each small division is $\frac{1}{100}$ of a metre. $\frac{1}{100}$ m is written as 0·01m.
The arrow is pointing to 4 small divisions after 2·6. It is pointing to 2·64m.

## DISCUSSION EXERCISE 12:4

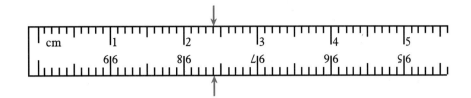

What measurements are given by each of the pointers? **Discuss.**

Trace the scale.

**Discuss** where to put pointers which give readings of 1·7cm, 4·1cm, 5·0cm, 96·5cm, 95·8cm, 99·3cm.

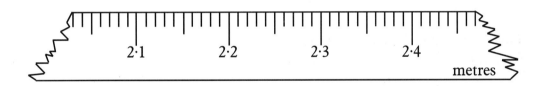

Trace the scale.

**Discuss** where to put pointers which give readings of 2·3m, 2·35m, 2·42m, 2·17m, 2·08m, 2·29m.

- Where are scales, such as those shown above, used? **Discuss.**

- Think of other scales which can be read to the nearest tenth or hundredth of a unit. **Discuss.**

## EXERCISE 12:5

1. Find the measurements given by the pointers A, B and C.

**(a)**

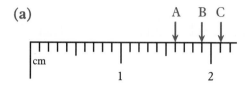

**(b)**

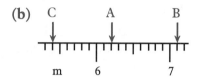

**(c)**

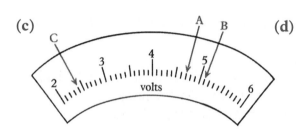

**(d)**

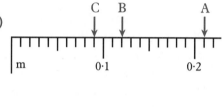

**(e)**

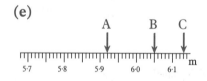

**(f)**

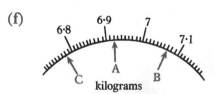

**(g)**

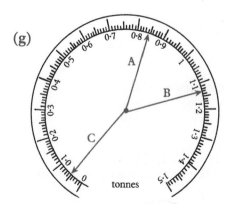

2. Find the length of these.

(a)

(b)
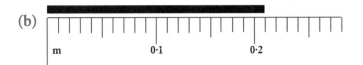

(c)

3. Hussan was in a long jump competition.
   After each jump, a marker was put in the pit at the point where he had landed. A tape was used to measure the length of the jump.
   These diagrams show the markers for Hussan's three jumps.

(a) How long was Hussan's first jump?

(b) Which jump was the longest? How long was this jump?

(c) How long was Hussan's last jump?

**Review 1**    What measurement is given by the pointers?

(a)

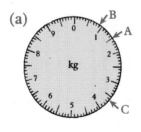

(b)

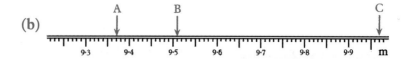

**Review 2**    What temperature is shown on this thermometer?

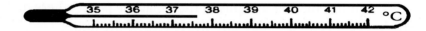

---

## PROJECT

1. Choose some units of measurement from: *l*, m*l*, t, kg, g, km, m, cm, mm.
   Collect pictures of things you would measure in each of your chosen units.
   Make a poster or a collage of these pictures.

2. Do a report on the units of measurement used in a sport or leisure activity.
   Ideas are: football, car racing, billiards, horse racing etc.
   Use reference books to help in this project.

3. Think about a car or other motor vehicle.
   List as many measurements as you can about this vehicle. Be sure to include things such as fuel tank capacity and engine size.

---

**DID YOU KNOW** that many years ago, the Babylonians believed that the sun moved around the earth?

They believed the sun took 360 days to go round the earth once.

Because of this they decided to use 360 units for anything to turn through a complete circle. These units are called degrees.

---

## DISCUSSION EXERCISE 13:1

- Yasmin is facing East.
  Yvonne says "Yasmin, face South."

  **Discuss** other ways in which Yvonne could have given Yasmin the same instruction.

- Which things on the following photos are vertical? Which things are horizontal? **Discuss.**

- Look around you in the classroom. Make a list of the things that are vertical. Make a list of the things that are horizontal. **Discuss** your lists with your group or class.

## PERPENDICULAR and PARALLEL LINES

This line can be called AB, since it runs from A to B.
It can also be called BA, since it runs from B to A.

**Parallel lines** are always the same distance apart.
Parallel lines never meet.
In this diagram the line AB is parallel to the line CD.
We write AB//CD. The symbol // is read as
"is parallel to."

We often put arrows on lines to show
that they are parallel.

**Perpendicular lines** are at right angles to each other. In each diagram below the line AB is perpendicular to the line CD.

We write AB ⊥CD. The symbol ⊥ is read as "is perpendicular to."

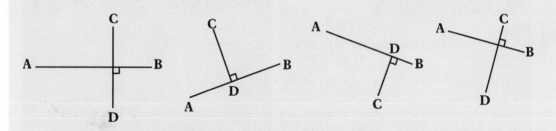

## DISCUSSION and PRACTICAL EXERCISE 13:2

- Which lines in these photos are parallel? Discuss.

  Which lines in these photos are perpendicular? Discuss.

- Take a walk around your school buildings or grounds. Make a list of the parallel lines and the perpendicular lines that you see.

Parallel and perpendicular lines can be drawn with a set square. One angle of a set square is a right angle.

If you do not have a set square, you can make a paper one as shown in the following diagrams.

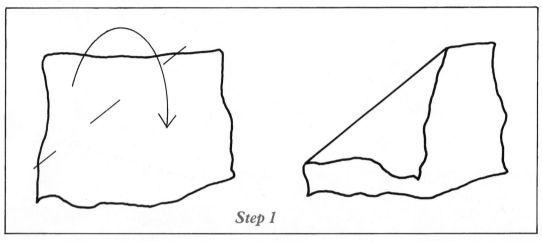

*Step 1*

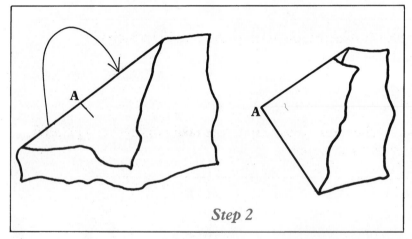

*Step 2*

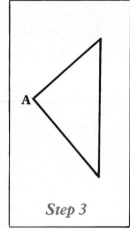

*Step 3*

*Step 1*  Take a piece of paper.
Fold one corner over to form a straight edge.

*Step 2*  Fold the paper again so that half of the straight edge is exactly on top of the other half.

*Step 3*  Trim away the untidy edges of the paper.
Staple all the thicknesses of paper together.

## DISCUSSION EXERCISE 13:3

• How can you use your set square to find which of these lines are perpendicular? **Discuss.**

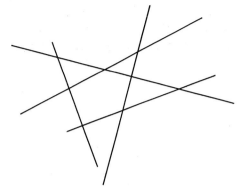

•

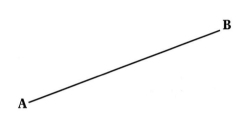

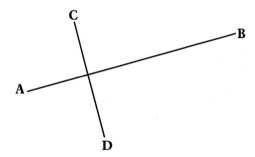

Draw a line AB.
How could you use your set square to draw the line CD which is perpendicular to AB? **Discuss.**

• The diagrams below show the steps that can be taken to draw two parallel lines, using a ruler and a set square.

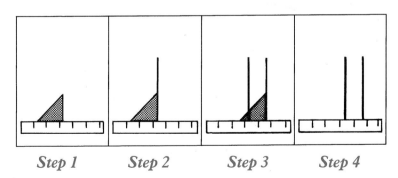

*Step 1*     *Step 2*     *Step 3*     *Step 4*

**Discuss** these steps. As part of your discussion, draw some parallel lines using your ruler and set square.

- The diagrams below show the steps that can be taken to draw a line through a point C that is parallel to the line AB.

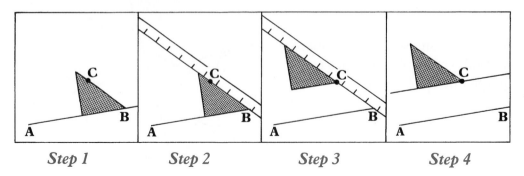

*Step 1*　　　　*Step 2*　　　　*Step 3*　　　　*Step 4*

**Discuss** these steps. (*Hint*: in Step 3, the set square slides along the ruler.)

- How can you use your set square to find which of these lines are parallel? **Discuss.**

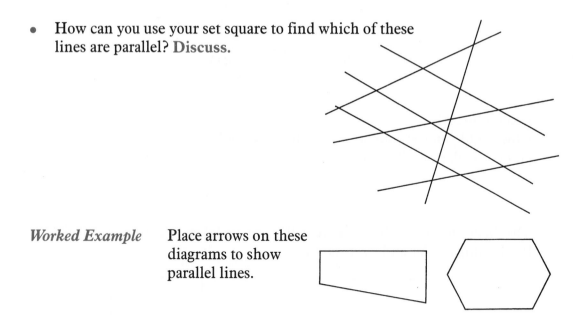

*Worked Example*　　Place arrows on these diagrams to show parallel lines.

*Answer*　　On the second diagram there are 3 pairs of parallel lines. A single arrow has been used to mark one pair, a double arrow to mark another pair and a triple arrow to mark the third pair.

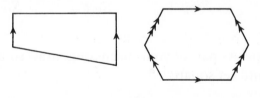

## EXERCISE 13:4

1.

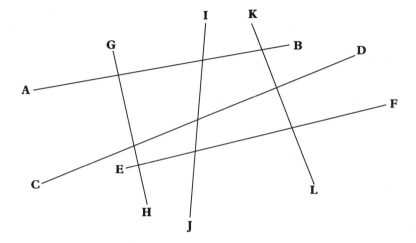

Name all the pairs of lines that are perpendicular.

2.

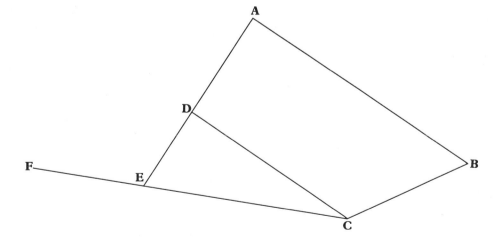

Which of the symbols, // or ⊥, go in the gaps?

(a) AB ... AD        (b) BA ... CD        (c) DC ... AE

**3.**

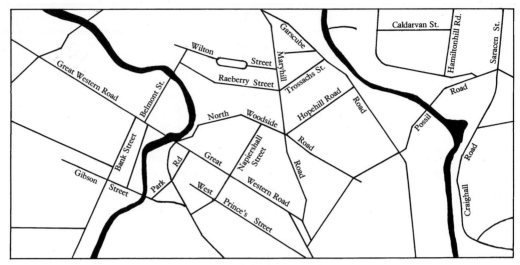

(a) Which street is parallel to Hopehill Road?

(b) Which road is parallel to West Prince's Street?

(c) Is Gibson Street parallel to any part of Wilton Street?

**4.** Trace this diagram.
Place right-angle signs to show perpendicular
lines and arrows to show parallel lines.

**5.** (a) Trace this line.
Use your set square to draw a perpendicular line
through D.

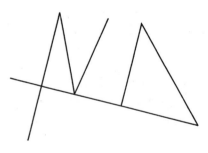

(b) Repeat **(a)** for this line.

(c) Trace this diagram.
Use your set square to draw the line through D
that is parallel to AB.

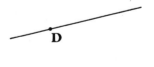

(d) Repeat **(c)** for this diagram.

6. Copy these two boxes.

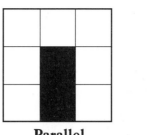

**Parallel**

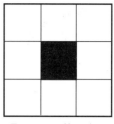

**Perpendicular**

Decide whether the two red lines are parallel or perpendicular.
If you decide they are parallel, place the letter beside the diagram in the "Parallel" box.
If you decide they are perpendicular, place the letter beside the diagram in the "Perpendicular" box.

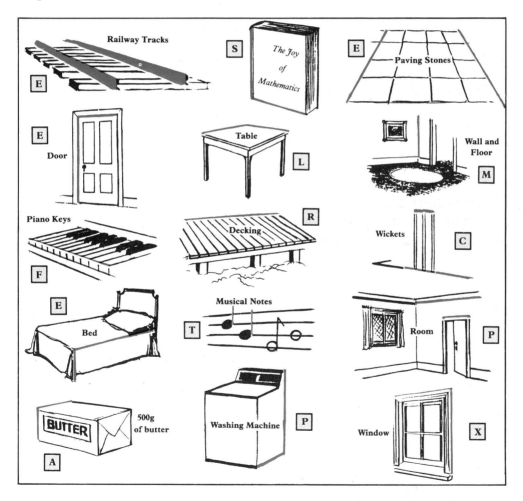

Use the letters in the "Parallel" box to make a word.
Use the letters in the "Perpendicular" box to make a word.

**Review 1**

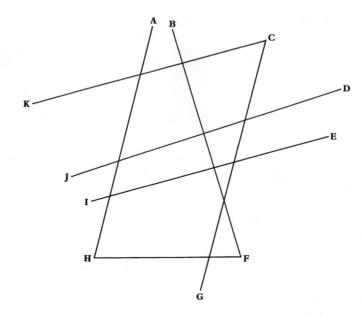

(a) Name all the pairs of parallel lines.

(b) Name all the pairs of perpendicular lines.

**Review 2**  Trace these diagrams.
Place arrows to show parallel lines and right-angle signs to show perpendicular lines.

 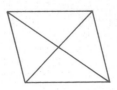 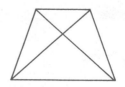 

**Review 3**  Trace this diagram.
Use your set square to

(a) draw the line through C that is perpendicular to AB

(b) draw the line through D that is parallel to AB.

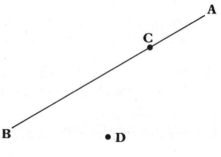

# VERTICAL and HORIZONTAL LINES

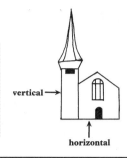

A **vertical line**, or surface, is perpendicular to the surface of the earth.

A **horizontal line**, or surface, is parallel to the horizon.

## DISCUSSION EXERCISE 13:5

Not all of the following statements are true.
**Discuss** these statements.

*A line which is perpendicular to a horizontal line must be vertical.*

*A vertical line can never be perpendicular to another vertical line.*

*Two horizontal lines can be perpendicular.*

## PRACTICAL EXERCISE 13:6

Decorators use a plumb line to make sure things are vertical. What things?
Builders use a spirit level to make sure things are horizontal or vertical.
What things?

1. Use a spirit level either in or outside the classroom to check whether floors, walls, window frames etc. are horizontal or vertical.

2. Make a plumb line using a heavy weight on the end of a rope or thick string. Decide what you could use this plumb line for, either in or outside the classroom.
   Use the plumb line.

## PROJECT

Make a logo, for your group or class or school, using parallel lines and shading.

**DID YOU KNOW**  that a square can be made into a triangle?

## DISCUSSION and PRACTICAL EXERCISE 14:1

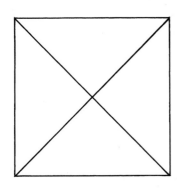 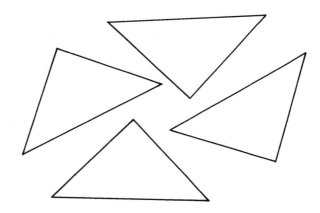

This square has been cut into 4 triangles.
Trace these triangles onto heavy paper or thin cardboard.
**Discuss** how to fit these 4 pieces together to make a large triangle.

• Make your own shape puzzle as follows.

  *Step 1*  Draw a shape; for instance, a triangle.

  *Step 2*  Draw lines across your shape to make smaller shapes.

  *Step 3*  Cut out the smaller shapes.

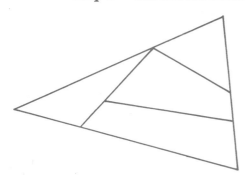 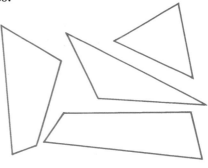

Ask another student to make your original shape from the pieces.

# CONSTRUCTING CIRCLES

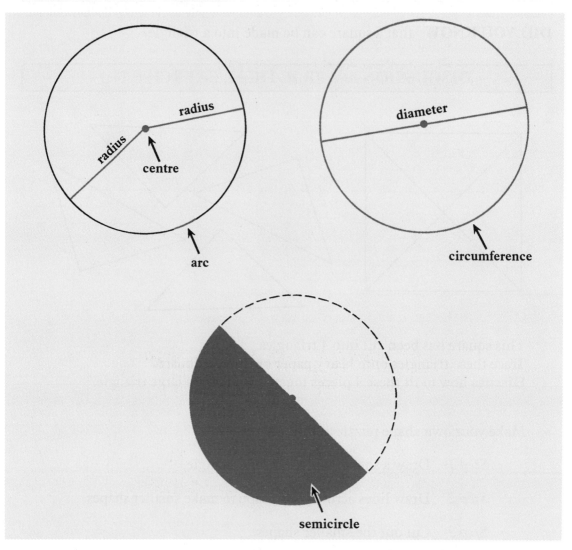

A circle may be drawn with a **compass**.
To draw a circle follow these steps:

*Step 1*   Place the compass point on the paper.

*Step 2*   Holding the compass firmly at the top, rotate
the compass pencil on the page.

The compass pencil draws the circumference of the circle. The compass point is
placed at the centre of the circle.

## DISCUSSION and PRACTICAL EXERCISE 14:2

1.  Draw a line, 12cm long.
    Place marks along this line, each one 2cm apart.
    Use your compass to draw the circles shown below.

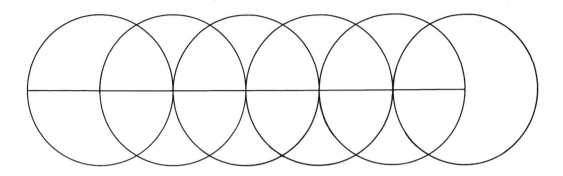

How have the patterns below been made? **Discuss.**

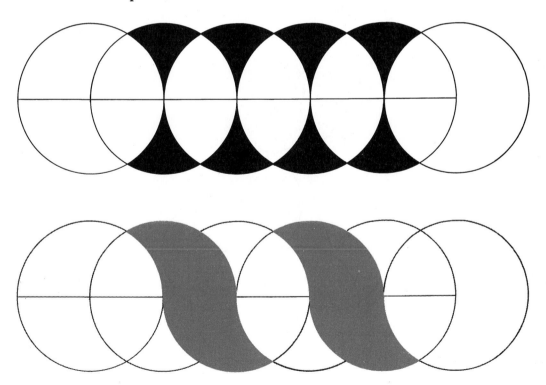

Make patterns of your own.

2. How have these patterns been made? **Discuss.**
   As part of your discussion, draw these patterns.

3. Draw some circle patterns of your own.

   Colour your patterns.

4. This design has been made using semicircles.

   How has this design been drawn? **Discuss.**

5. Make a design using semicircles.

## INVESTIGATION 14:3

**CIRCLE CIRCUS**

How many different patterns can you make by drawing 2 circles?
(Two examples are shown.) **Investigate.**

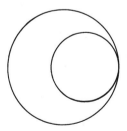 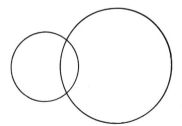

**What if** the circles were the same size?

**What if** there were 3 circles?

**What if** . . .

# CONSTRUCTING SQUARES, RECTANGLES, TRIANGLES

Squares and rectangles can be constructed using a set square and ruler.

## DISCUSSION EXERCISE 14:4

- Draw a line, 4cm long.
  This line is to be one edge of a square.

  How could you finish this square, using your set square and ruler? Discuss with your group or class.

- Draw a line, 5cm long.
  This line is to be one edge of a rectangle
  which is 5cm long and 3cm wide.

  Using your set square and ruler, how could you finish this rectangle?
  Discuss.

- Practise drawing rectangles and squares, using your set square and ruler.

  How could you check the accuracy of your drawings?
  Discuss.

- The lines drawn from one corner to the
  opposite corner are called diagonals.

  Did you talk about these in your discussion of
  ways to check the accuracy of your drawings?

Triangles may be constructed using a **compass and ruler**.

For instance, to construct a triangle with sides 5·5cm, 3cm, 3·8cm take these steps.

Step 1   Draw a line 5·5cm long.

Step 2   Open the compass out to 3cm.
Place the compass point on the left-hand end of the line.
Draw an arc.

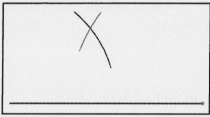

Step 3   Open the compass out to 3·8cm.
Place the compass point on the right-hand end of the line.
Draw an arc which crosses the arc drawn in Step 2.

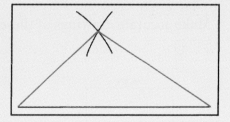

Step 4   Finish the triangle.

## EXERCISE 14:5

1.  Use your set square and ruler to make accurate drawings of:

    (a) a square with 44mm sides

    (b) a rectangle of length 8cm and width 6cm.

    Measure the length of the diagonals in each. Give your answers to the nearest mm.

2. Use your set square and ruler to make accurate drawings of these.

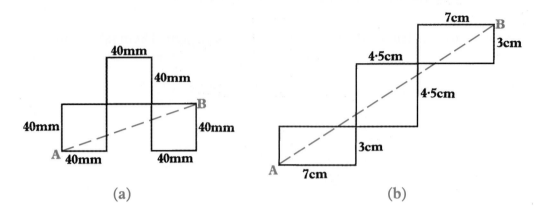

(a)                                               (b)

On your drawings, measure the length of AB. Give your answers to the nearest mm.

3. Use your compass and ruler to accurately draw triangles with sides of these lengths.

   (a) 7cm, 5·5cm, 5cm       (b) 6cm, 6·4cm, 5cm       (c) 5·5cm, 4·8cm, 3·6cm

   (d) 5cm, 3·8cm, 3·8cm     (e) 5cm, 5cm, 5cm

4. Make accurate drawings of these.

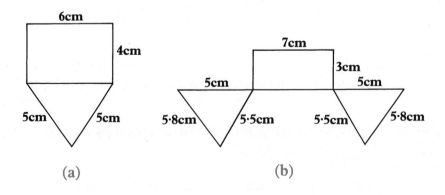

(a)                                               (b)

Review 1   Use your compass and ruler to draw a triangle with sides of 6·4cm, 6cm, 4·7cm.

**Review 2**    Use your set square, ruler and compass to accurately draw this diagram.

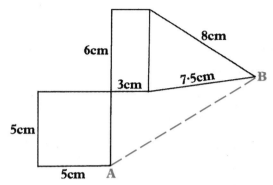

On your drawing, measure the length of AB. Give your answer to the nearest millimetre.

## INVESTIGATION 14:6

### A TRIANGLE OR NOT A TRIANGLE

1.  Is it possible to draw triangles with the following sides?

    | | | | |
    |---|---|---|---|
    | **1.** | 5cm | 3cm | 2cm |
    | **2.** | 4cm | 4cm | 3cm |
    | **3.** | 5cm | 3cm | 3cm |
    | **4.** | 7cm | 3cm | 3cm |

    Investigate. As part of your investigation test the statement "The sum of any two sides of a triangle must be greater than the third side."

2.  How many different triangles could be drawn using any three of the following lengths for the sides?

    8cm    7cm    6cm    5cm    4cm    3cm

    Investigate.

## INVESTIGATION 14:7

### SHAPES from SQUARES

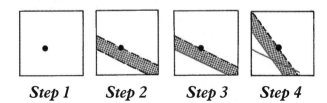

*Step 1*     *Step 2*     *Step 3*     *Step 4*

*Step 1*   Draw a large square, at least 10cm by 10cm.
          Mark a point near the centre of this square.

*Step 2*   Place your ruler across the square so the marked point is on one
          edge of the ruler.

*Step 3*   Draw a line along the *other* edge of the ruler.

*Step 4*   Move your ruler and repeat Steps 2 and 3.
          Continue to draw many lines in this way.

          What shape is made? **Investigate.**

          **What if you began with a rectangle?**

## DISCUSSION and PRACTICAL EXERCISE 14:8

- How could you accurately draw this diagram of a circle touching
  the sides of a square? **Discuss.**

  As part of your discussion, try to accurately draw a similar
  diagram.

- Make a design using circles within squares or squares within circles.

  Colour your design.

## JUST FOR FUN

1.

Take away 5 matchsticks to leave 3 squares of the same size.

2. Take away 8 matchsticks to leave 4 squares.

3.

By moving 2 matchsticks, make 7 squares.

**DID YOU KNOW** that an Easterly wind blows from the East? That is, it blows towards the West.

## DISCUSSION EXERCISE 15:1

-

  In what direction does a Northerly wind blow? What about a South-Easterly wind. **Discuss.**

- "The airport is 500km to the South," said the pilot.

  "I've planted wheat in the North-West field," said the farmer.

  "I've got to go South-West to get out of town," said the lorry driver.

  A pilot, a farmer and a lorry driver all might use compass directions. Think of other people who might use compass directions. How would they use them? **Discuss.**

- This is a weather-vane.
  What is it used for?

  If a weather-vane is pointing to North-East, in what direction is the wind blowing? **Discuss.**

## COMPASS DIRECTIONS

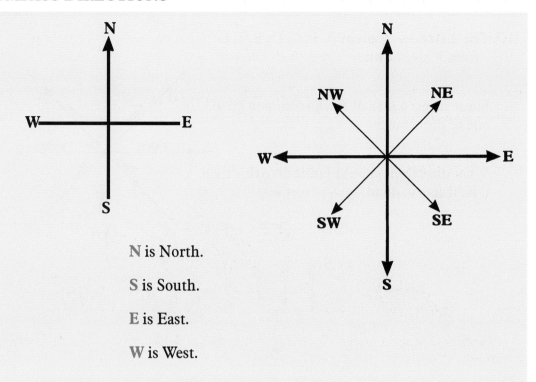

N is North.

S is South.

E is East.

W is West.

NE is North-East and is halfway between North and East.

NW is North-West and is halfway between North and West.

SE is South-East and is halfway between South and East.

SW is South-West and is halfway between South and West.

*Example*

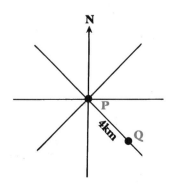

Instructions for getting from P to Q could be: From P, go 4km in a SE direction.

## EXERCISE 15:2

1. The distances of towns A, B, C, D, E, F, G from P are shown.

   Jamie meets a man at P who wants to go to one of these towns.

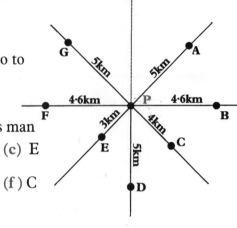

   What directions should Jamie give this man if he wants to go to (a) G   (b) A   (c) E

   (d) D   (e) F   (f) C

   (g) B?

2.

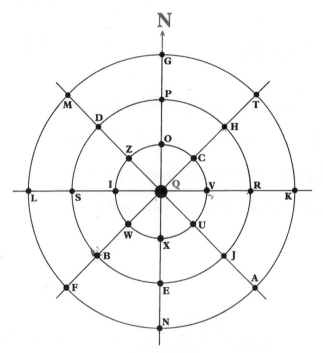

*The radii of the circles on this diagram are 2km, 4km, 6km.*

From Q which point is          (a) 4km NW          (b) 2km South

(c) 4km SE          (d) 2km NE          (e) 6km SW          (f) 6km East

(g) 2km West          (h) 4km NE          (i) 2km SE          (j) 6km NE?

**Review**

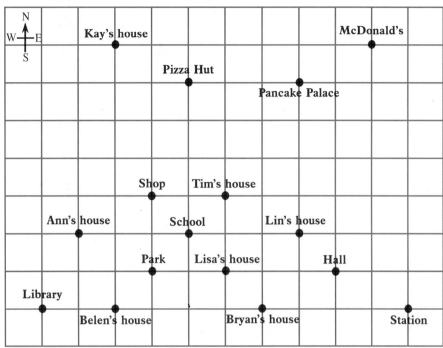

*Each square is 100m long.*

(a) Whose house is East of the school?

(b) Whose house is South-West of the school?

(c) How far is the Station from the Library?

(d) What is North-West of the school?

(e) What is North-West of the hall?

(f) Whose house is South-East of Kay's House?

(g) From the station, Sally walks North-West. Does she pass the Pancake Palace?

(h) From school, Imke walks South for 200m, then West for 400m, then North-West. Could Imke reach the shop without changing direction again?

(i) From her house, Kay walks West for 100m. She then walks South to her friend's house, then she walks to school with her friend. How far does Kay walk altogether?

## DISCUSSION EXERCISE 15:3

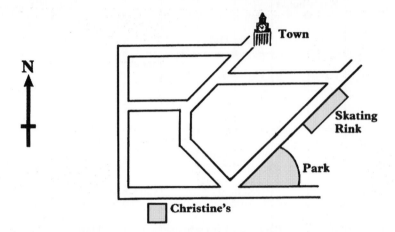

Christine was trying to tell her friend how to get to her house from town.
What directions could she give her friend?
Is there more than one way to get to Christine's house from town?
Which is the shortest way? Which is the longest? **Discuss.**

---

A Northerly wind blows *from* the North.

A Southerly wind blows *from* the South.

A North-Westerly wind blows *from* the North-West, and so on.

---

*Example*   A leaf blown by a South-Westerly wind would move in a North-Easterly direction.

*Example*   On the map at the top of this page, the Skating Rink is North-East of the Park.

## EXERCISE 15:4

1.

This is a map of a fun park.

What direction is  (a)  Monster Mouth from Market Square

(b)  Music Land from Valley of Doom

(c)  Haunted House from Market Square

(d)  Playtown from Market Square

(e)  Playtown from Haunted House

(f)  Monster Mouth from Valley of Doom

(g)  Valley of Doom from Haunted House

(h)  Market Square from Playtown?

2.  **Use the Map in Question 1.**

From Market Square what is     (a) East     (b) North-East

(c) South     (d) North-West?

3.

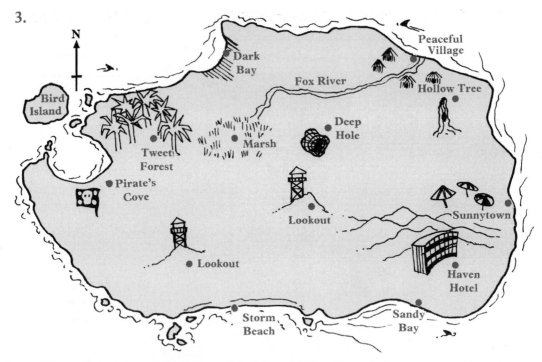

There is treasure hidden on this island. The directions are given below.
Where is the treasure hidden?

From Pirates Core go North-East to a place of many birds
From here go East to a swamp
Go South to where there will be thunder and lightning
Go North-West to a place where you can see all around
Go East to a place where you could sleep the night
Go South-West but take your shoes off or they'll fill with sand
Go North to where the river ends
Go South-East and you will find a perfect place for hiding *Treasure*

4. The roads are closed because of snow. A helicopter is taking food to these farms.

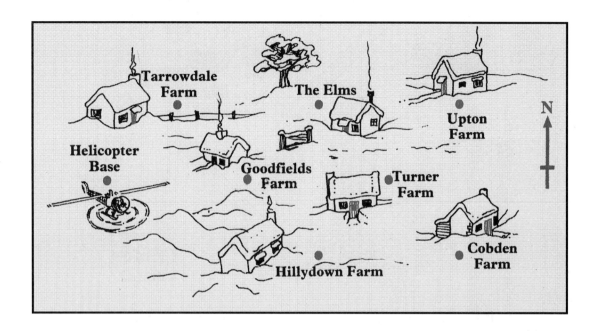

(a) Write down the directions you would give to the pilot of the helicopter so that it goes to every farm.

(b) Write down a different set of directions for the pilot so that the helicopter goes to every farm.

(c) One day the helicopter pilot uses a smaller helicopter. This helicopter can only carry enough food for 4 farms. It will have to make two journeys. Write down the directions you would give the pilot.

5. Amber is walking to school. There is a South-West wind blowing. A leaf blows across Amber's path. In what direction is the leaf moving?

6. Ahmed is walking South-East. The sun is shining straight into his eyes. He turns clockwise a quarter turn.

(a) What direction is he walking in now?

(b) Is the sun shining on to his left or right side?

# Review

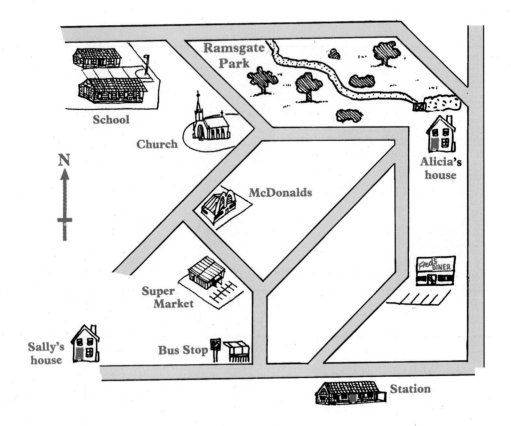

Sally gave her friend directions on how to get to her house from school.

She said "Walk East from the school until you come to Ramsgate Park,
        then walk South-East to the Church,
        then walk South-West to McDonalds,
        then ..."

(a) Write down the rest of Sally's directions.

(b) Write down the directions to get from Sally's house to McDonalds.

(c) Write down the directions to get from school to Fred's Diner.

(d) Write down the directions to get from Alicia's house to Sally's house.

(e) Sally goes North-East from McDonalds. When she reaches the church she turns clockwise. Is she going to school or Alicia's house?

## JUST FOR FUN

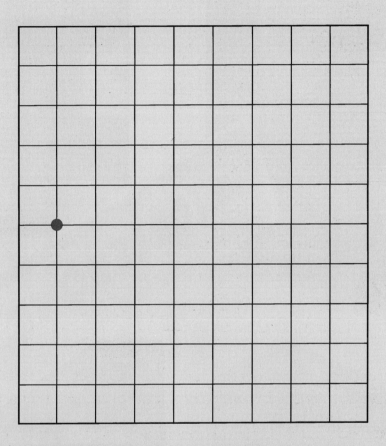

Copy this diagram. What shape is drawn by beginning at the dot and following these directions?

1. North-East through 2 squares
2. North 1 square
3. South-East through 2 squares
4. East 2 squares
5. North-East through 1 square
6. East 1 square
7. South-West through 1 square
8. South 5 squares
9. West 2 squares
10. North-East through 1 square
11. North 2 squares
12. West 2 squares
13. South 3 squares
14. West 2 squares
15. North-East through 1 square
16. North 2 squares
17. North-West through 1 square
18. South-West through 1 square
19. North-West through 1 square.

**DID YOU KNOW**   that a desk calendar can be made from two cubes?

## DISCUSSION EXERCISE 16:1

Two cubes are to be used as a desk calendar.
Any date, from 1 to 31, must be able to be shown.

What numbers must be painted on the sides of the cubes? Discuss.

## MAKING CUBES

Many cardboard boxes are made as follows.

A shape is cut from a flat piece of cardboard.
This shape is then folded into a box shape.
Glue and/or staples and/or sticky tape is then used along the edges to make sure the box doesn't collapse.

The shape that is cut from the flat piece of cardboard is called a net.

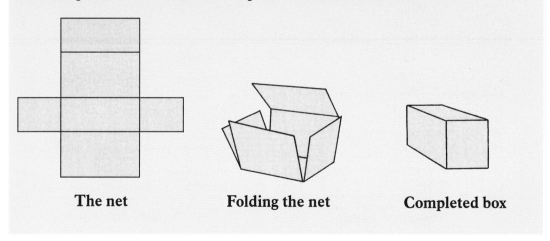

| The net | Folding the net | Completed box |

## DISCUSSION and PRACTICAL EXERCISE 16:2

Bring empty cardboard boxes to school. Cereal boxes are good.

Cut these boxes open to find their nets.

Could the same box be cut open in different ways to get different nets? **Discuss.**

This net can be folded to make a cube.
The fold lines are shown dotted.

When drawing a net for a cube, it is a good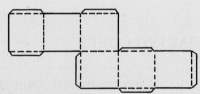
idea to draw tabs (flaps) on every second edge.

Before folding a net into a cube crease along all the fold lines.
These are shown as dotted lines in the diagram.

The net for a cube can be drawn on squared paper or on square dot paper.
The net can also be constructed using a ruler and set square.

Large nets are easier to fold than small nets.
Squares with edges of 2cm make a net of a good size.

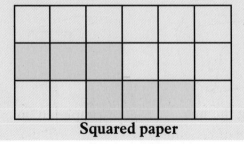

**Squared paper**

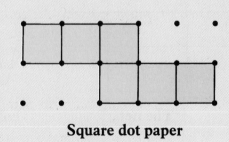

**Square dot paper**

# DISCUSSION and PRACTICAL EXERCISE 16:3

- Which of these nets will fold to make a cube? Discuss.

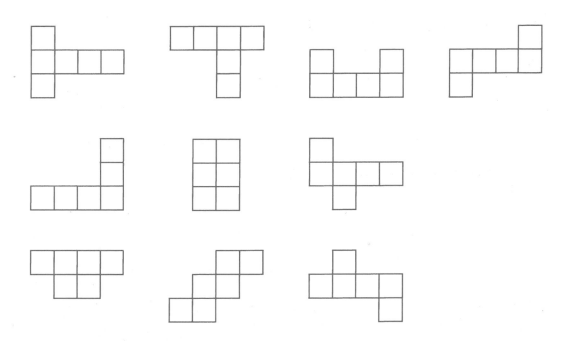

As part of your discussion you could make the nets.

Remember to    1.   make each edge a good length

                 2.   add tabs to every second edge

                 3.   crease before you fold.

- Draw a net, other than those given above or on **page 202**, that will fold into a cube.

  Discuss your net with your group or class.

- Make 4 cubes by drawing and folding nets.

  What shapes can you make using just 3 of the cubes? Discuss.

  What shapes can you make using all 4 of the cubes? Discuss.

## DISCUSSION and PRACTICAL EXERCISE 16:4

● When this box is rotated horizontally, "Jack in the box" can be read.
The same words can be read if the box is rotated vertically.

Will the net shown make this box?

Design nets that will make this box. **Discuss.**
As part of your discussion, make the box *after* writing the words on the net.

|  |  | IN |  |
|------|------|------|------|
| JACK | IN | THE | BOX |
|  |  | JACK |  |

● The number of dots on opposite faces of a die always add to 7. (The plural of die is dice.)

This net can be used to make a die.

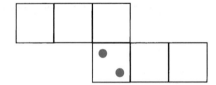

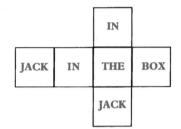

**Discuss** how many dots will be on each of the other faces. As part of your discussion, make the die *after* putting the dots on the net.

## PRACTICAL EXERCISE 16:5

1. Make 27 small cubes using one of the nets on this page.

Colour 9 of these red, 9 blue and 9 yellow.

Make these into a 3 × 3 × 3 cube (as shown at the bottom of the next page) in which no row or column has two cubes of the same colour.

2.  The 7 pieces shown make a set of Soma cubes.
    One piece is made from three cubes, the rest are made from four cubes.

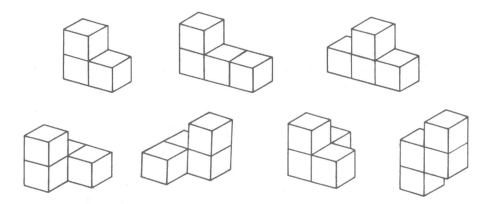

Use the 27 small cubes to make these 7 pieces.

## INVESTIGATION 16:6

**SHAPES from SOMA CUBES**

You will need a set of Soma cubes for this investigation.

You could use the set you made in **Practical Exercise 16:5.**
You could make a set by glueing together wooden or plastic cubes.
You could make a set from Multilink.

Can all 7 pieces be used to make this $3 \times 3 \times 3$ cube?
Investigate.

Can some of the pieces be used to make a $2 \times 2 \times 2$
cube? Investigate.

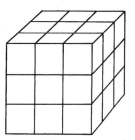

What other shapes can you make using all 7 pieces? Investigate.

What if you used just some of the pieces?

# JUST FOR FUN

**Equipment:**   a sheet of A4 paper
8 paper clips
1 pair of scissors

Each group uses just this equipment to make the tallest possible "tower" in a set time.

A time limit of about 15 minutes is suggested.

**DID YOU KNOW**  that identical shapes are also known as congruent shapes?

**PAPER FOLDING**

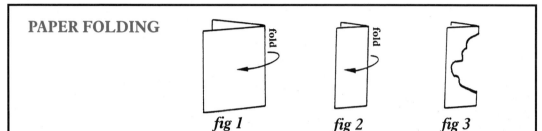

fig 1          fig 2          fig 3

Take a piece of paper (15 cm by 10 cm is a good size).
Fold it in half twice, each time folding the right-hand side over to the left-hand side — see *fig 1* and *fig 2*.
Draw and cut out a design which begins near the bottom of the right-hand side and ends near the top of the right-hand side — see *fig 3*.
Unfold your paper. Describe the cut out shapes.

**What if** you folded the paper vertically three times, instead of twice?

**What if** you drew a shape on the folded paper that began at the bottom and finished on the right-hand side?

**What if** you drew a shape on the folded paper that began on the right-hand side and finished on the left-hand side?

**What if** you cut out a shape without cutting near the edges?

**What if** you folded the paper once vertically, then once horizontally?

**What if** . . .

How would you fold and cut out to make touching congruent shapes such as those shown below? **Investigate.**

## CONGRUENT SHAPES

If a tracing of one shape will fit exactly over another shape, the shapes are said to be congruent.

**Congruent shapes** are the same shape and size.

---

## DISCUSSION EXERCISE 17:2

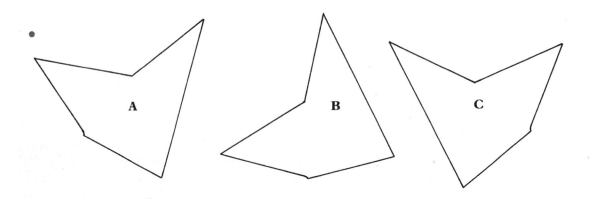

● 

These three shapes are congruent.
Trace shape A.
Does this tracing fit exactly onto shape B?
How can this tracing be made to fit exactly onto shape C?
**Discuss.**

●

Three of these shapes are congruent. Which ones? **Discuss.**

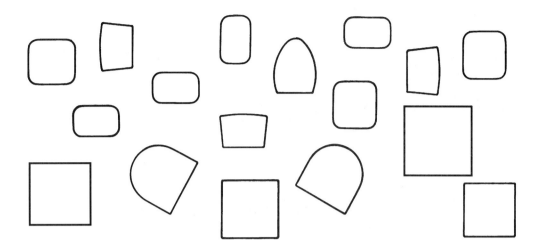

**Discuss** which of these shapes are congruent.

Melanie was making 20 felt dolls for sale at the school fair.
She made a "pattern" from heavy paper.
She then used this "pattern" to cut out all the dolls.

Think of other examples where a "pattern" might be used to make congruent shapes.

**Discuss** with your group or class.

**Congruent shapes** are identical.

Congruent shapes    — are the same shape

                        — are the same size

                        — have angles of the same size

                        — have sides of the same length

Congruent solids have angles and sides and faces of the same size.

*Worked Example*

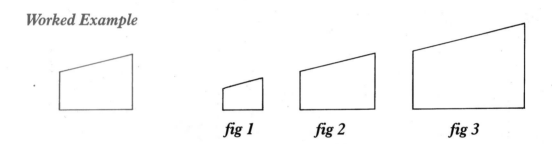

Which of the black shapes is congruent to the red shape?

*Answer*    *fig 2* is congruent to the red shape since it is identical. All its angles and its sides are the same size as those in the red shape.

*Worked Example*

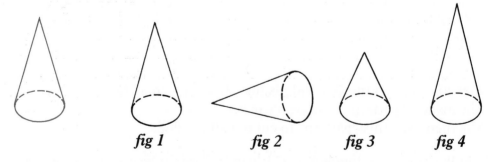

Which of the black shapes are congruent to the red shape?

*Answer*    Both *fig 1* and *fig 2* are congruent to the red shape.

# EXERCISE 17:3

1.

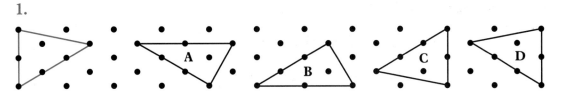

Which shapes are congruent to the red shape?

2.

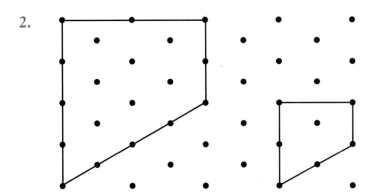

Explain why these two shapes are not congruent.

3.

All of these shapes cover the same number of squares.

Are any of these shapes congruent?

4. Name all the shapes that are congruent to the red shape.

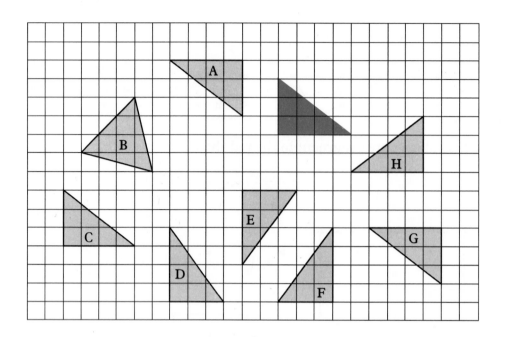

5.

Name the congruent shapes. (Be sure to use tracing paper.)

6. Are any of these solids congruent? If so, which ones?

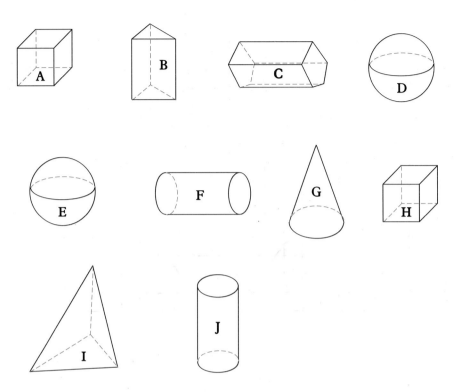

7. Name all the congruent shapes in this diagram.
   You may want to trace each shape first. Then try to fit your tracings over other shapes.

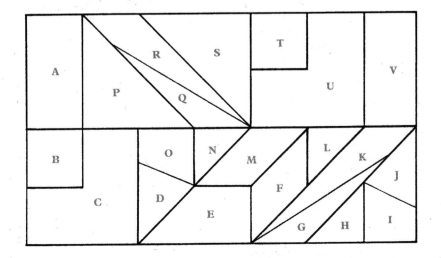

**Review 1** Name the congruent shapes.

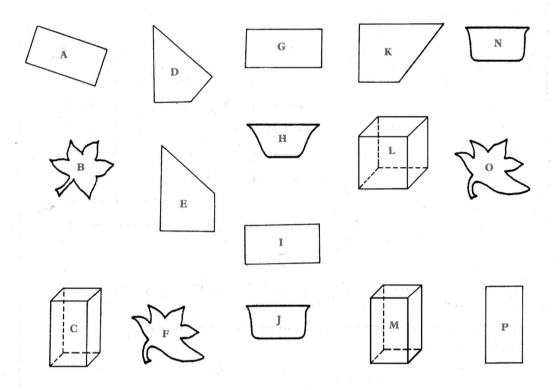

**Review 2** Which of these shapes are congruent? (Be sure to use tracing paper to help answer this question.)

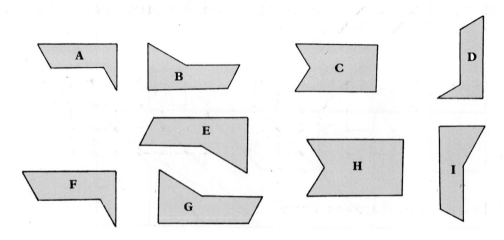

## INVESTIGATION 17:4

### DIVIDING a SQUARE

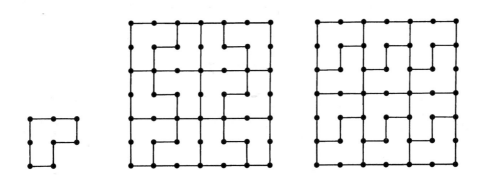

Both of the 6 × 6 squares have been divided into 12 shapes, all congruent
with the shape on the left.
How else could you divide a 6 × 6 square into 12 of these congruent
shapes? **Investigate.**

What if the square was an 8 × 8 square?
What if the square was a 10 × 10 square?
What if the shape to be divided was a 12 × 8 rectangle?
What if ...

What if a square or rectangle was to be divided into shapes congruent with
those shown below?

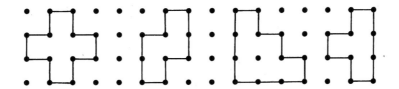

What if another shape was chosen?

## PRACTICAL EXERCISE 17:5

1.  Draw and cut out 24 congruent triangles.
    You may like to use different coloured paper; perhaps cut out 8 triangles in each of three colours.

    Arrange these triangles into an interesting pattern.

Instead of drawing the 24 triangles, you may like to make them by drawing 3 squares, then paper folding. This is shown below.

Fold in half twice to get the horizontal and vertical creases. Then fold diagonally to get the diagonal creases.

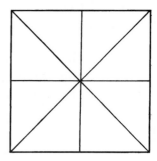

You could use triangles of any shape.
You could cut one triangle from cardboard, then draw around this to get 24 congruent triangles.

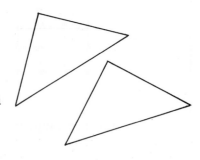

2. The grey and pink triangles are the same shape and size as the red triangle but drawn in different positions.

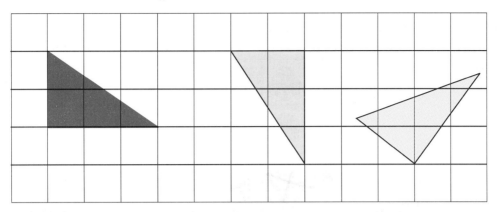

On grid paper, draw 5 more triangles the same shape and size as the red triangle.

Draw each in a different position.

On grid paper, draw each of the following shapes in some different positions.

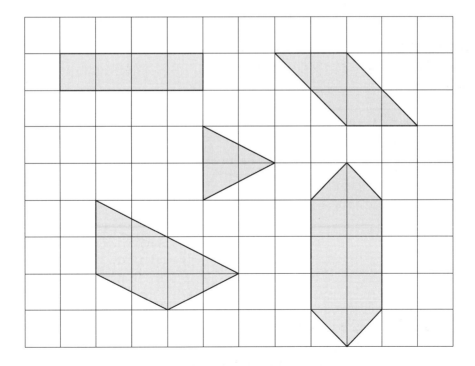

Choose a shape. On grid paper, draw this shape in different positions to make a pattern. You may like to colour your pattern.

## PUZZLE 17:6

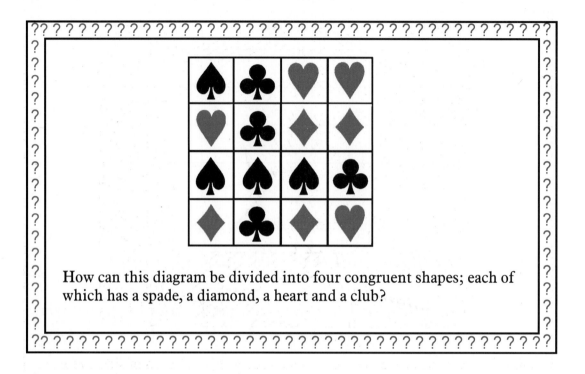

How can this diagram be divided into four congruent shapes; each of which has a spade, a diamond, a heart and a club?

## PRACTICAL EXERCISE 17:7

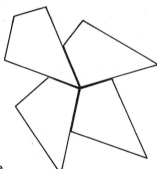

Make an interesting 4-sided shape.

Cut your shape out of thin cardboard.

Draw around your shape to make an interesting pattern.

# JUST FOR FUN

On cardboard, draw four congruent squares A, B, C, D each of side 2 cm; one square J of side 4 cm; five congruent rectangles E, F, G, H, I measuring 4 cm by 2 cm.

Draw a rectangle 10 cm by 8 cm and place the 10 pieces on this rectangle as shown.

Without moving any piece off the rectangle at anytime, move the pieces so that piece J is in the space that pieces B and C are in at the beginning.

*Note*  Much patience is needed.

**DID YOU KNOW** that many objects which are pleasing to the eye involve a repeated pattern?

## DISCUSSION EXERCISE 18:1

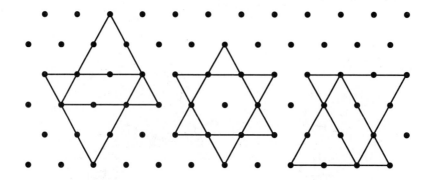

Each of these diagrams is made from the same two identical triangles.

In what other ways could you arrange these triangles? Which diagrams involve a repeated pattern? **Discuss.**

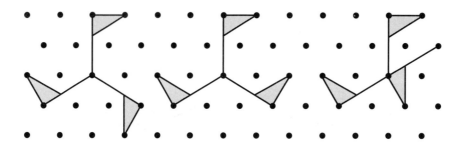

Three "flags" are arranged in different ways in these diagrams.

How else could these "flags" be arranged? Which arrangements involve a repeated pattern? **Discuss.**

# ROTATIONAL SYMMETRY

A shape has rotational symmetry if it fits onto itself more than once during a complete turn.

To check if a shape has rotational symmetry we can take the following steps.

*Step 1*  Trace the shape onto tracing paper.

*Step 2*  Use the point of a pencil to firmly hold the tracing paper over the shape.

*Step 3*  Rotate the tracing paper.

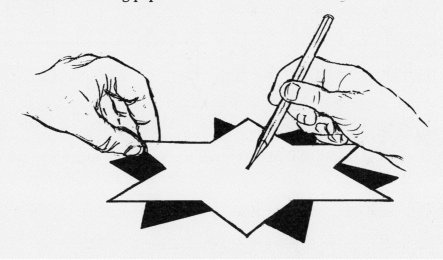

## DISCUSSION EXERCISE 18:2

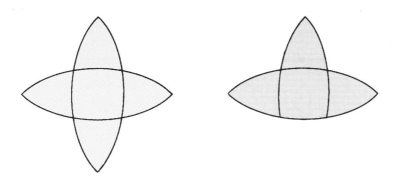

The diagram on the left has rotational symmetry. The diagram on the right does not. Why not?

**Discuss** with your group or your class.

The number of times a shape will fit onto itself during one complete turn is called the **order of rotational symmetry.**

## EXERCISE 18:3

1.

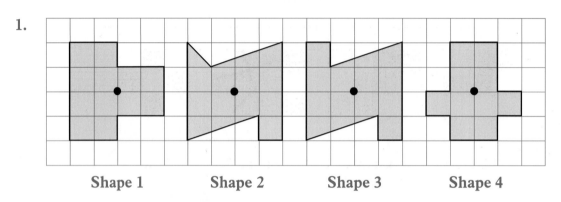

| Shape 1 | Shape 2 | Shape 3 | Shape 4 |

Which of these shapes will fit onto itself if given a half turn about the dot?

2.

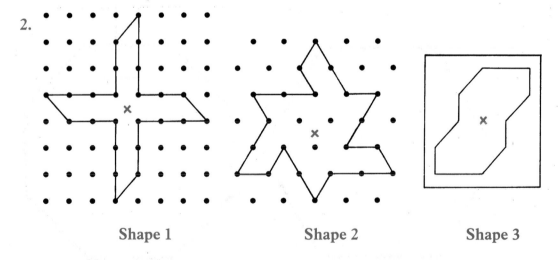

| Shape 1 | Shape 2 | Shape 3 |

(a) When rotated about the x, which of these shapes will fit onto itself after each $\frac{1}{3}$ turn?

(b) What is the order of rotational symmetry of each of the shapes?

3. What is the order of rotational symmetry of this shape?

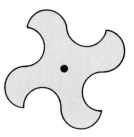

4.

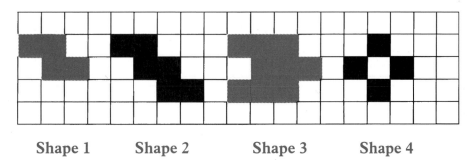

     **Shape 1**       **Shape 2**        **Shape 3**       **Shape 4**

    (a) Which of these shapes does *not* have rotational symmetry?

    (b) What is the order of rotational symmetry of the other shapes?

5.

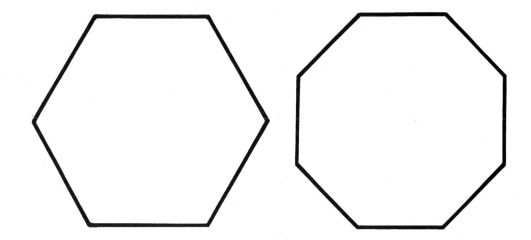

Trace one of these shapes or draw a square.

On the shape of your choice, draw a pattern that has rotational symmetry.

Review

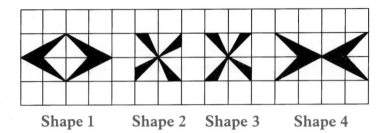

Shape 1        Shape 2     Shape 3        Shape 4

(a)  Three of these shapes have rotational symmetry. Which three?

(b)  Which shape has rotational symmetry of order 4?

## INVESTIGATION 18:4

### COLOURING REGIONS

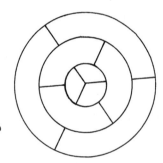

This shape has rotational symmetry.

Colour the 9 parts of this shape so that no two touching parts are the same colour.

What is the least number of colours that can be used? **Investigate.**

**What if** the shape is still to have rotational symmetry? What is the least number of colours now? **Investigate.**

## PRACTICAL EXERCISE 18:5

1.  Collect objects which have rotational symmetry. Make a classroom display of these.

    Stamps, vases, jewellery, coins, playing cards are some of the things you could collect.

2.  Look for rotational symmetry in objects in your school grounds. Include things such as flowers, bicycle wheels etc.

    Make a list of the objects.

# REFLECTING in a MIRROR LINE

## DISCUSSION EXERCISE 18:6

- Place a mirror along the dotted line.
  Look at the shape, in the mirror.

  Is the part that appears to be behind the mirror congruent with that part in front of the mirror?
  What else do you notice? **Discuss.**

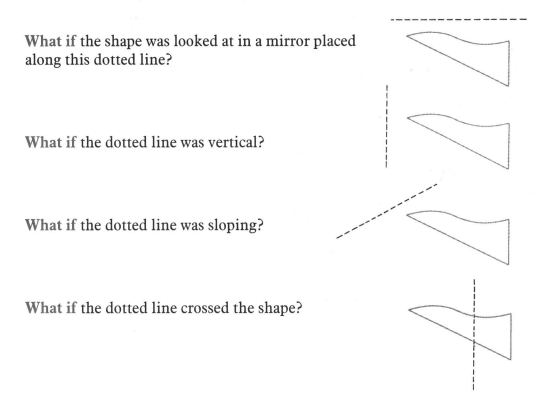

  **What if** the shape was looked at in a mirror placed along this dotted line?

  **What if** the dotted line was vertical?

  **What if** the dotted line was sloping?

  **What if** the dotted line crossed the shape?

- Draw a shape in your book.
  Draw a dotted line.
  Look at the shape in a mirror placed on the dotted line.
  Draw what you see in the mirror.
  **Discuss** with your group. As part of your discussion, discuss how you could accurately draw what you see in the mirror.

# GAME 18:7

**MIRROR ACTIONS: a game for 2 students or a group**

**Game for 2 students**

One student is the leader.

The two students face each other.

The leader "takes up a position" with his or her head, arms and hands.

The other student must position his or her head, arms and hands so they are a mirror image of the leader's.

The leader now changes the position for the other student to "mirror".

When the student fails to correctly "mirror" the leader's position the two students swap roles.

**Game for a group**

One student is the leader. This student "takes up a position".

One of the other students tries to "mirror" this position.

The leader now changes the position for the student to "mirror".

The leader and the student continue like this until the student fails to correctly mirror the leader's position. The student is then replaced by another of the students in the group.

The leader changes when each of the students in the group has had a turn to "mirror" the leader's positions.

The student who correctly "mirrored" more of the leader's positions than anyone else becomes the new leader.

What you see when you look at the reflection of a shape in a mirror is called the image of the shape.

The line where the mirror is placed is called the mirror line.

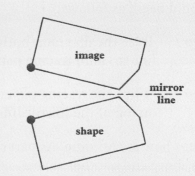

A shape and its image are congruent.

A shape must be "flipped" over the mirror line to find the position of the image.

Each point on the image is the same distance from the mirror line as the corresponding point on the shape.

*Examples*

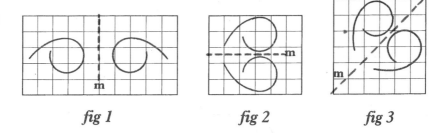

*fig 1*        *fig 2*        *fig 3*

*fig 1*   shows a shape reflected in a vertical mirror line **m**.

*fig 2*   shows a shape reflected in a horizontal mirror line **m**.

*fig 3*   shows a shape reflected in a sloping mirror line **m**.

## PRACTICAL EXERCISE 18:8

1.  Draw a shape.
    Imagine this shape reflected in a mirror. Draw the imagined reflection.
    Check by looking at the reflection of the shape in a mirror.

2.  Take a mirror into the grounds of your school.
    Look at objects reflected in the mirror.
    Draw these reflections.

## DISCUSSION EXERCISE 18:9

A reflection may be drawn using tracing paper.

We could begin as follows:

*Step 1*   Trace the diagram (both the shape and the mirror line **m**) onto tracing paper.

*Step 2*   "Flip" the tracing paper. Place the traced mirror line on top of the mirror line **m**.

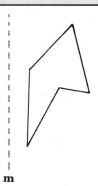

**Discuss** how to continue. As part of your discussion, draw the reflection of the shape above and of other shapes.

## EXERCISE 18:10

1.   Copy these shapes. Reflect them in the mirror line **m**.

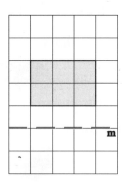
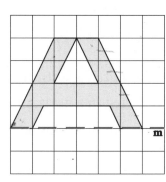

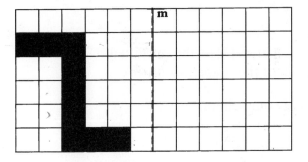
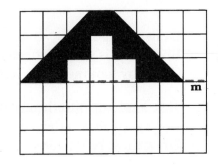

2. Reflect each of these shapes in the mirror line **m**.
   Write down the coordinates of the vertices of the image shapes.

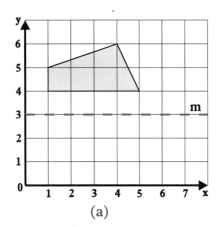
(a)

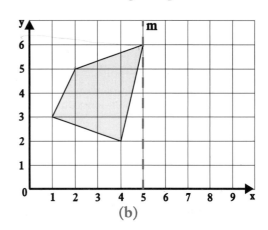
(b)

3.

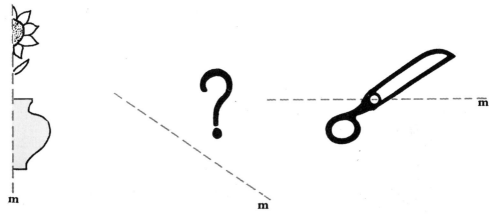

(a) "Insect **3** is a reflection of insect **2** in the mirror line *l*."
Is this statement true?

(b) Copy and complete:
Insect **2** is a reflection of insect . . . in the mirror line . . .

(c) There is another reflection shown in this diagram. Describe this reflection.

4. Copy these diagrams.
   Draw the reflection of each shape in the mirror line **m**.

**Review1**   Copy these diagrams.
Draw the reflection of each shape in the mirror line **m**.

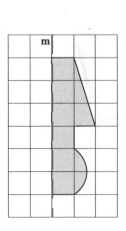 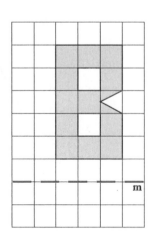 

**Review2**

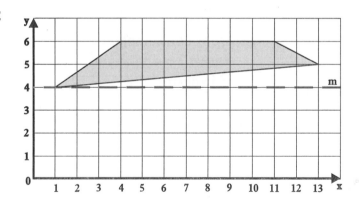

This shape is to be reflected in the mirror line **m**.
What are the coordinates of the image shape?

---

## PROJECT

Make up a board game.
Design the board for this game. Include rotational symmetry and reflection as part of your board design.

You may also like to include translation.

---

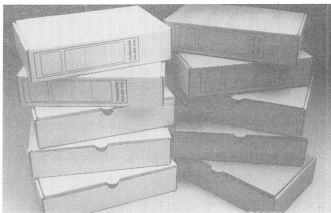

**DID YOU KNOW** that the distance around the outside of shapes may be different even though each shape takes up the same amount of space?

## DISCUSSION EXERCISE 19:1

Five square tables may be arranged as shown.
Twelve people may be seated at this arrangement if only one person may be seated along each side.

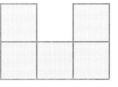

In what other ways could these tables be arranged if each table must share a side with at least one other table? How many people could be seated? **Discuss.**

## PERIMETER

The distance right around the outside of a shape is called the **perimeter**.

Perimeter is measured in mm, cm, m or km.

*Example*    The perimeter of this shape is 2 + 1·6 + 2·8 + 1·2 + 3·9 km = 11·5km

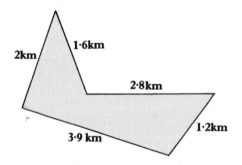

| **DISCUSSION EXERCISE 19:2** |
| --- |

• Which of mm, cm, m or km would be used to measure these? **Discuss.**

the perimeter of the school grounds

the perimeter of Greater London

the perimeter of a milk stain on a carpet

• Think of some perimeters which would be measured in km.

Think of some perimeters which would be measured in m.

Think of some perimeters which would be measured in cm.

Think of some perimeters which would be measured in mm.

**Discuss** these with your group or class.

## EXERCISE 19:3

1. Measure the perimeter of these. Give your answer to the nearest mm.

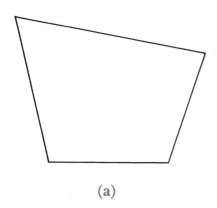

        (a)

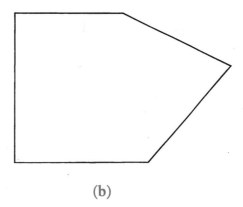

        (b)

2. The distance between dots is 1cm.
   Without measuring, find the perimeters of the shapes.

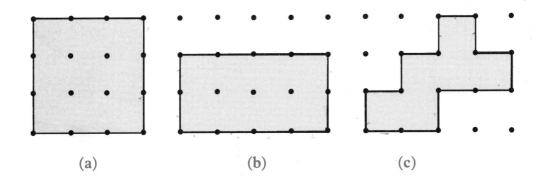

   (a)           (b)           (c)

3. Calculate the perimeter of these.

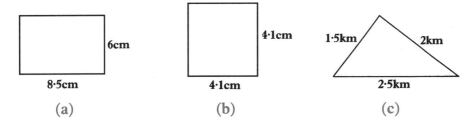

   8·5cm         4·1cm         2·5km

   (a)           (b)           (c)

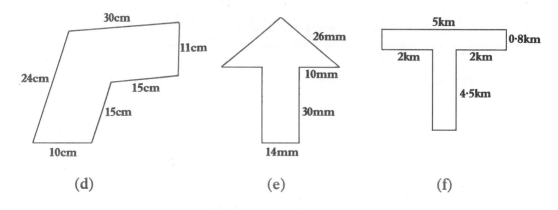

(d)                (e)                (f)

4. Find the perimeter of   (a) a rectangle which measures 82mm by 50mm

   (b) a square of side 6·2cm.

5. This is the sketch that Verity made of the park beside her home.

   Verity calculated the perimeter.

   What answer should Verity get?

6.    A car race is 10 laps of this circuit.

   To the nearest km, how far does a car travel if

   (a) it finishes the race

   (b) it fails to take the bend at B on its second lap?

7. Which is the longer route from A to B: the route along

   the red lines or the route along the black lines?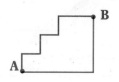

**Review 1**   Measure the perimeter of this shape. Give
your answer to the nearest mm.

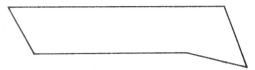

**Review 2**   Find the perimeter of a square of length 7·3cm.

**Review 3**   A swimming pool measures 33m by 10m.

Amy swims 10 lengths of this pool. Her friend
swims 4 laps around the perimeter of the pool.

Who swam the greater distance, Amy or her
friend?

## INVESTIGATION 19:4

### SAME PERIMETER

These rectangles both have perimeter of 16cm.

What other rectangles have perimeter of 16cm? **Investigate.**

What if the perimeter was 12cm?

What if the perimeter was 25cm?

What if . . .

## COUNTING SQUARES to find AREA

The amount of surface a shape covers is called its area.

This square is lcm long and lcm wide.
The area of this square is called 1 square centimetre.
We write 1 square centimetre as lcm².

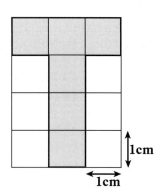

*Example*   This shape covers 6 squares.
We could say: area of this shape = 6 squares.

Since the area of each square is lcm², the area
of the shape is 6cm².

Some units for measuring area are mm², cm², m², km².

A square with side lmm has an area of 1 square millimetre. This is written as 1 mm².

A square with side lm has an area of 1 square metre. This is written as lm².

A square with side lkm has an area of 1 square kilometre. This is written as lkm².

## PRACTICAL EXERCISE 19:5

On heavy paper or thin cardboard draw thirty squares, each with sides of lcm.

Use 16 of these squares to make a rectangle. How many different rectangles can you make?

Make shapes, other than rectangles, using the 16 squares.

What if you used 24 squares?

What if . . .

## DISCUSSION EXERCISE 19:6

● ☐ The sides of this square are 1cm long.
The area of this square is 1cm².

▫ The sides of this square are 1mm long.
The area of this square is 1mm².

Why can we not show a square of area 1m² on this page?
How big is a square of area 1m²? **Discuss.**

How big is a square of area 1km²?
**Discuss.**

● With which unit of area (mm², cm², m², km²) would it be sensible to measure these? **Discuss.**

the area of Scotland          the area of a pin head
the area of a ruler          the area of a classroom
the area of a lawn          the area of a football pitch

● What else might be measured in km²?
What else might be measured in m²?
What else might be measured in cm²?
What else might be measured in mm²? **Discuss.**

The **area** of a shape may be estimated as follows.

*Step 1*   Draw an outline of the shape on squared paper.

*Step 2*   Count the squares the shape covers.

When counting the squares, count the whole squares first. Then count each square that is more than half covered as 1 square. Do not count the squares that are less than half covered.

*Example*

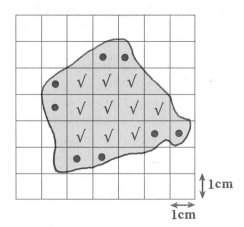

Each whole square is marked with a √.
Squares that are more than half covered are marked with a •.
Counting the √ and • we get 18 squares in total.

The estimated area is 18cm².

The previous method gives a good estimate if there are about equal numbers of squares that are less than half covered and more than half covered.

If this is not so, a better way to estimate is as follows: Count the whole squares. Group partly covered squares together to make whole numbers of squares.

*Example*

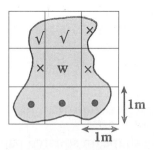

The only whole square is marked as w.
Together the √ squares make about 1 square.
Together the × squares make about 1 square.
Together the • squares make about 2 squares.

Estimated number of squares covered = 5.

Estimated area = 5m².

## EXERCISE 19:7

1. A mural of a fish was made for an outside wall of an aquarium.
   What approximate area does the fish cover?

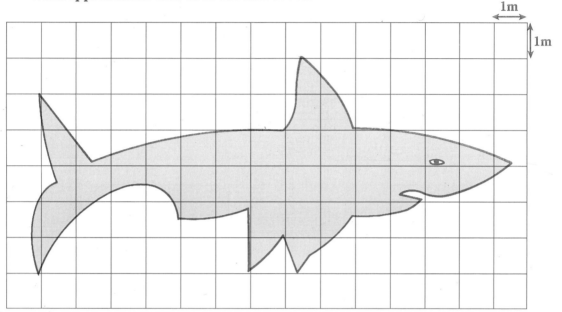

2. An island is shown below.
   What is the approximate area of this island?

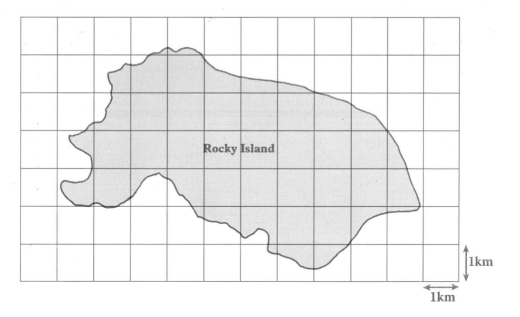

3.  Count squares to find the areas of the grey shapes.

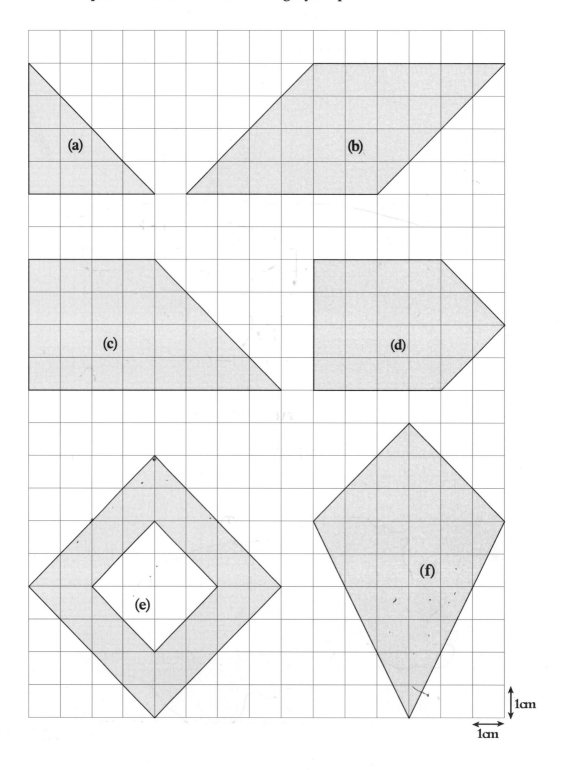

**Review 1** Jan made soft toys for the school fête using this pattern. Count squares to estimate the area of the pattern.

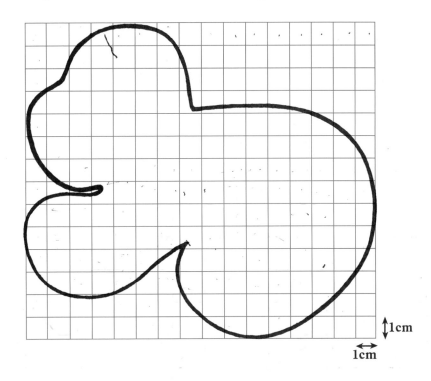

1cm
1cm

**Review 2** Count squares to find the area of these shapes.

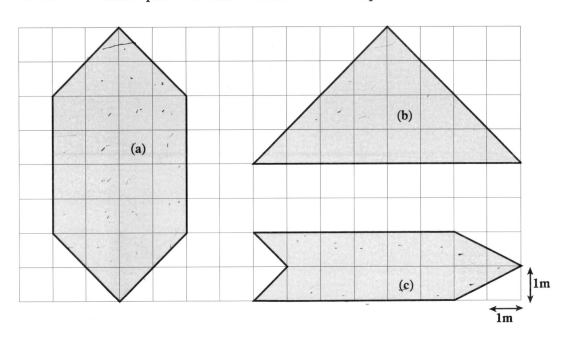

(a) (b) (c)

1m
1m

## PRACTICAL EXERCISE 19:8

1. Draw an outline of your hand on squared paper.
   Count squares to estimate the area.

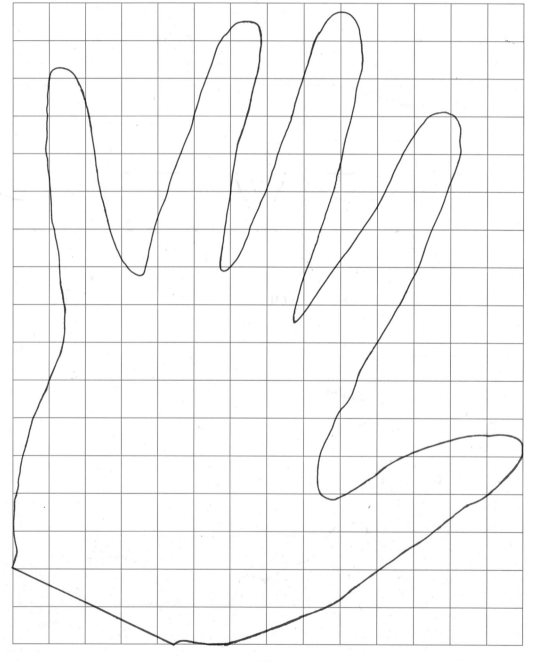

2. Make a statement such as:

    *My left hand is bigger than my right hand.*
    *My friend and I both take the same size shoe so our feet are the same size.*

    Test your statement by counting squares to find areas.

3. Count squares to find the area of objects in the school grounds. You could find the area of leaves etc.

    Instead of picking a leaf, then drawing its outline on one centimetre squared paper, you could place a transparent grid (drawn up in one centimetre squares) over the leaf.

## INVESTIGATION 19:9

### SQUARES WITHIN SQUARES

Susan claims that she can fit 100 squares of side 1mm into this
1 centimetre square.
She said that $1cm^2 = 100mm^2$.
Is Susan correct? **Investigate.**

Investigate the statement "$1m^2 = 100cm^2$."

## COUNTING CUBES to find VOLUME

The **volume** of a shape is the amount of space it takes up.

1 cubic centimetre is the amount of space this cube takes up. 1 cubic centimetre is written as $1cm^3$. We say that the volume of a cube of side 1cm is $1\,cm^3$.

Units of volume are $mm^3$, $cm^3$, $m^3$.

## DISCUSSION EXERCISE 19:10

- How large is lmm³?
  How large is lm³? **Discuss.**

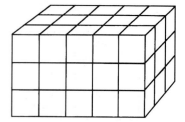

- Suppose each of the cubes in this shape has a side
  of lcm.
  What is the volume of each of the cubes?

To find the volume of the shape we could count all the cubes. We could also
begin as follows.

*Step 1*   Count the cubes in one layer.

*Step 2*   Count the number of layers.

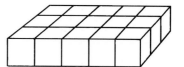

**Discuss** how to continue to find the volume of the shape.

## EXERCISE 19:11

**In each of the shapes in this exercise, the small cubes measure lcm by lcm
by lcm.
Find the volume of the shapes.**

1.

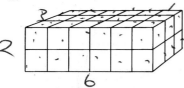

2.   $3 \times 1 \times 2$

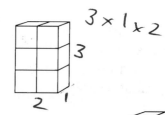

3.

4.

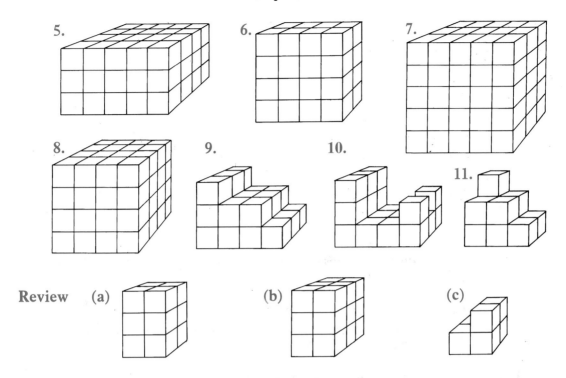

5.    6.    7.

8.    9.    10.

11.

Review    (a)    (b)    (c)

---

## INVESTIGATION 19;12

---

### SURFACE AREA and VOLUME

**Build each shape from centimetre cubes.**

The volume of this shape is 4cm³.
The area of all of the surfaces (top, bottom,
front, back and both sides) is 18cm².

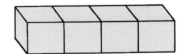

What is the surface area of these?
What is the volume?
Can four centimetre cubes be
arranged in other ways?

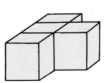 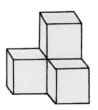

Investigate to find the arrangement which has the smallest surface area.

Investigate to find the arrangement which has the greatest surface area.

*continued . . .*

*. . . from previous page*

What if we began with three cubes?

What if we began with five cubes?

## JUST FOR FUN

A shape can be made, using these clues.

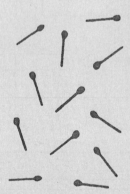

**Clue 1** There are 12 matchsticks in the shape.

**Clue 2** The matchsticks do not overlap.

**Clue 3** No line on the shape is shorter than two matchsticks.

**Clue 4** There are two triangles in the shape.

**Clue 5** The triangles share a side.

**Clue 6** The triangles are not congruent.

**Clue 7** One of the triangles has a perimeter of seven matchsticks.

**Clue 8** There is a 4-sided figure in the shape.

**Clue 9** The 4-sided figure has a perimeter of nine matchsticks.

Make the shape.

1.

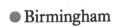

(a) What direction is Brighton from Portsmouth?

(b) Which town is North-East of London?

(c) What direction is Portsmouth from Beccles?

(d) Which town is South-East of Royston?

(e) Which city, or town, is North-West of London?

(f) Which direction is Portsmouth from London?

(g) Which city, or town, is approximately North-West of Portsmouth?

**2.**

| mm cm m km mg g kg t m*l* *l* sec min |
|---|

Which unit of measurement would be used for the following? Choose from the units given in the box.

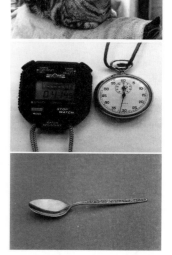

(a) the length of the Suez Canal

(b) the thickness of a compact disk

(c) the mass of coal mined in a week

(d) a cat's weight

(e) the height of a mountain in Nepal

(f) the amount of oil used by a car in one year

(g) the time to run a sprint race

(h) the capacity of a teaspoon

(i) the mass of icing sugar on a bowl of strawberries

**3.** Two of these nets can be folded to make a cube. Which two?

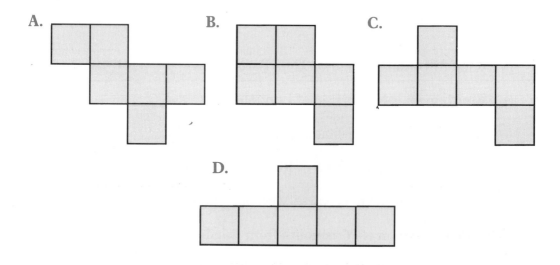

A.    B.    C.

D.

4. Copy these diagrams.
   Reflect each shape in the mirror line **m**.

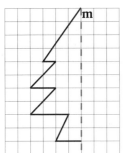 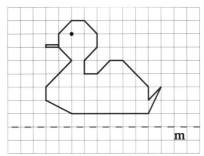

5. Leanne used this pattern for the material to be glued on the seat of a model yacht.

   Count squares to find the area of this material.

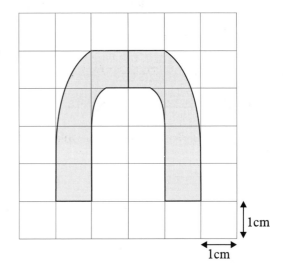

6.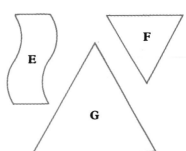

   Name shapes that **(a)** are congruent

   **(b)** have rotational symmetry.

**7.**

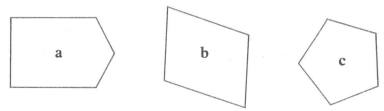

Trace these.

Place arrows to show parallel lines.
Place right-angle signs to show perpendicular lines.

**8.** Use your compass, set square and
ruler to accurately draw this.
On your drawing, measure the
lengths of AB and CD. Give your
answers to the nearest millimetre.

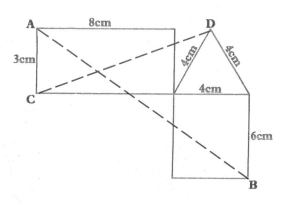

**9.**

There is 1 cm between each dot.

**(a)** What is the perimeter of the shape?

**(b)** What is the area of the shape?

10.

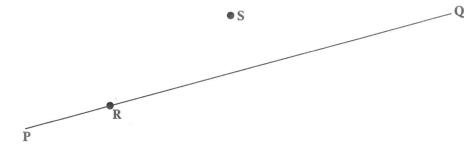

Copy this diagram.

Use your set square and ruler to

(a) draw the line through R that is perpendicular to PQ

(b) draw the line through S that is parallel to PQ.

11.

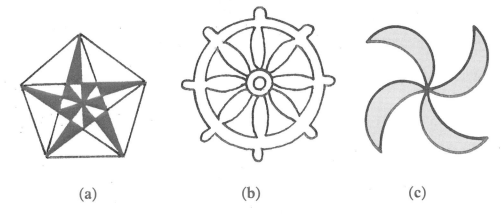

(a)                          (b)                          (c)

What is the order of rotational symmetry of these?

12. Each small cube measures 1cm by 1cm by 1cm.
    What is the volume of each shape?

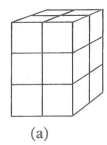       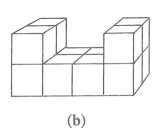

(a)                          (b)

13. Are these shapes congruent?

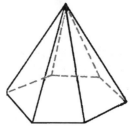 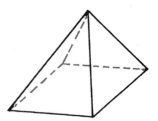

14. What reading is given by the pointers?

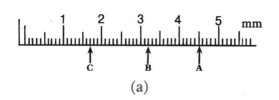

(a)

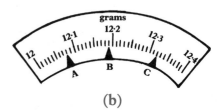

(b)

15. Which of the cubes does this net make? Is there more than one answer?

**A.**          **B.**          **C.**          **D.**          **E.**

16. The wind is blowing from the South-West. In which direction is this hat moving?

17.

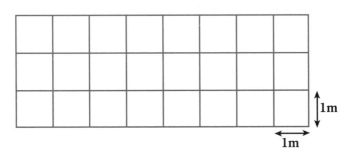

1m

1m

The area of this rectangle is 24m². The perimeter is 22m.

(a) Another rectangle has the same area as the one shown but perimeter of 20m. Draw this rectangle.

(b) Another rectangle has the same perimeter as the one shown but area of 28m². Draw this rectangle.

18. (a) Copy this shape. Reflect it in the mirror line **m**.

(b) What are the coordinates of the images of the points A, B and C?

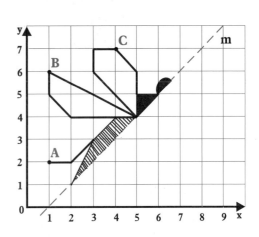

# HANDLING DATA

## REVISION

### GRAPHS and FREQUENCY TABLES

This **bar chart** or **bar graph** shows the number of hours of sunshine one week. On Monday there were 3 hours of sunshine, on Tuesday 4 hours, on Wednesday 4 hours, on Thursday 3 hours, on Friday 8 hours, on Saturday 6 hours and on Sunday 5 hours.

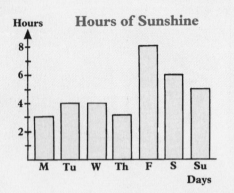

Hours of Sunshine

This **pictogram** shows the number of teams in a sports competition.

9 teams are playing Football.
6 teams are playing Hockey.
5 teams are playing Badminton.

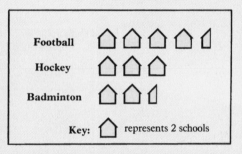

Sports Pictogram

Key: represents 2 schools

27  29  28  30  29  27  27  29  28  29  27  30  29  28  27  28  29  29  27

The figures in this list give the number of biscuits in 19 packets. These figures are summarised on the **tally chart**.

On the tally chart, a stroke is made as each figure is recorded (a diagonal stroke is used for every 5th entry). Once all the figures have been recorded, the strokes are added to get the frequency. Because this tally chart also has the frequency it can also be called a **frequency table**.

### Biscuits Tally Chart

| Number | Tally | Frequency |
|--------|-------|-----------|
| 27 | ~~||||~~ | | 6 |
| 28 | |||| | 4 |
| 29 | ~~||||~~ || | 7 |
| 30 | || | 2 |

*continued . . .*

*. . . from previous page*

| Transport | Walk | Cycle | Train | Bus | Car | Other |
|-----------|------|-------|-------|-----|-----|-------|
| Frequency | 6 | 2 | 3 | 5 | 3 | 1 |

The frequency table shows how the students in one class come to school. This information is also shown on the block graph below.

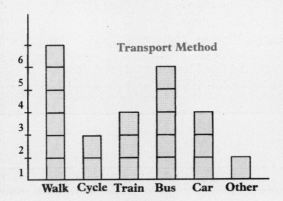

We can make conclusions from this graph.
For instance, the same number of students come to school by car as by train.

## DIAGRAMS

A class was surveyed about board games played.
This Venn diagram shows that
    4 played both Scrabble and Monopoly
    6 played Scrabble but not Monopoly
    9 played Monopoly but not Scrabble
    2 played neither Scrabble nor Monopoly.

This Carroll Diagram tells us about the weather in May.
It was cold and raining on 8 days, cold but not raining on 2 days, mild and raining on 5 days, mild and not raining on 16 days.

**May Weather**

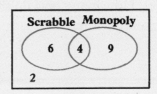

| | | |
|---|---|---|
| 8 | 2 | cold |
| 5 | 16 | mild |
| raining | not raining | |

*continued . . .*

*... from previous page*

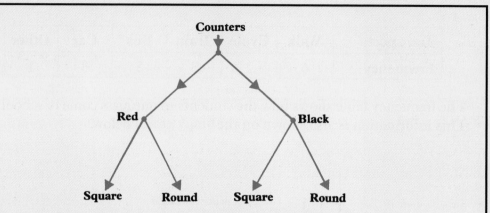

This **tree diagram** can be used to sort counters into:
red and square, red and round, black and square, black and round.

## REVISION EXERCISE

1. This graph shows the pets owned by a group of friends.

   (a) How many rabbits do these friends have?

   (b) Which pet is the most popular?

   (c) How many pets do these friends have altogether?

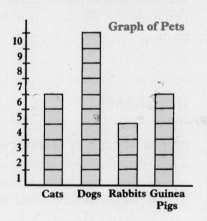

2. This diagram shows the people seen, on one day, by a dentist.

   (a) How many were women i.e. female adults?

   (b) How many were adults?

   (c) What else can you tell from this diagram?

   |  |  |  |
   |---|---|---|
   | 16 | 15 | Adult |
   | 4 | 6 | Child |
   | Female | Male | |

## 3.

**14.4 Television viewing[1] and radio listening: by age**
*United Kingdom* — Hours and minutes

| | Television viewing | | | | | Radio listening | | | | |
|---|---|---|---|---|---|---|---|---|---|---|
| | 1985 | 1986 | 1987 | 1988 | 1989 | 1985 | 1986 | 1987 | 1988 | 1989 |
| **Age groups** (hours:mins per week) | | | | | | | | | | |
| 4 – 15 years | 19:59 | 20:35 | 19:14 | 18:34 | 18:27 | 2:24 | 2:12 | 2:07 | 2:13 | 2:21 |
| 16 – 34 years | 21:36 | 21:10 | 20:03 | 20:36 | 20:34 | 11:42 | 11:24 | 11:18 | 11:40 | 12:07 |
| 35 – 64 years | 28:04 | 27:49 | 27:25 | 27:17 | 26:07 | 9:43 | 9:56 | 10:16 | 10:33 | 11:10 |
| 65 years and over | 36:35 | 36:55 | 37:41 | 37:25 | 36:29 | 8:04 | 8:27 | 8:44 | 8:49 | 9:00 |
| All aged 4 years and over | 26:33 | 25:54 | 25:25 | 25:21 | 24:44 | 8:40 | 8:40 | 8:52 | 9:12 | 9:46 |

1 Viewing of live television broadcasts from the BBC, ITV and Channel 4.

*Source: Broadcasters' Audience Research Board;*
*Audits of Great Britain;*
*British Broadcasting Corporation;*

**Source: Key Data 1991/92**

*From: Social Trends 1991, Table 10.6*

This table gives the average number of hours and minutes that are spent watching TV or listening to the radio.

(a) What does 19:59 mean?

(b) Does it seem that the time spent listening to the radio is increasing?

(c) Which age group watched TV for the longest time in 1989?

(d) One age group watched less TV in 1987 than in 1989. Which age group?

4. This pictogram shows the number of goals scored by hockey teams.

How many goals were scored by

(a) the Gaydene team

(b) the Merrihill team

(c) all of the 5 teams?

| Team | Goals |
|---|---|
| Harrowend | ⚒⚒⚒⚒⚒⁄ |
| Gaydene | ⚒⚒⚒⚒ |
| Merrihill | ⚒⚒⁄ |
| Cavely | ⚒⚒⚒⚒⚒⚒⚒ |
| Duneleigh | ⚒⁄ |
| **Key:** ⚒ represents 2 goals | |

5.

| Bird | Tally | Frequency |
|---|---|---|
| Robin | ~~||||~~ ||| | 8 |
| Thrush | |||| | |
| Sparrow | ~~||||~~ ~~||||~~ ||| | |
| Starling | ~~||||~~ ~~||||~~ | |
| Blackbird | ||| | |

Mardi collected data on the birds she saw on the school grounds on May 5th between 2 p.m. and 2.30 p.m.

(a) Copy and complete the frequency column.

(b) Draw a bar chart for this data.

(c) Decide what this bar chart tells you.

6.   **JUNE    Timetable: Dover to Calais**

| Dep. | M | T | W | T | F | S | S | M | T | W | T | F | S | S | M | T | W | T | F | S | S | M | T | W | T | F | S | S | M | T |
|---|---|---|---|---|---|---|---|---|---|---|---|---|---|---|---|---|---|---|---|---|---|---|---|---|---|---|---|---|---|---|
| Time | 1 | 2 | 3 | 4 | 5 | 6 | 7 | 8 | 9 | 10 | 11 | 12 | 13 | 14 | 15 | 16 | 17 | 18 | 19 | 20 | 21 | 22 | 23 | 24 | 25 | 26 | 27 | 28 | 29 | 30 |
| 07.05 | D | D | D | D | D | D | D | D | D | D | D | D | D | D | D | D | D | D | D | D | D | D | D | D | D | D | D | D | D | D |
| 08.05 | D | D | D | D | D | D | D | D | D | D | D | D | D | D | D | D | D | D | D | D | D | D | D | D | D | D | D | D | D | D |
| 09.05 |   |   |   | C | C | C |   |   |   |   | C | C | C |   |   |   |   | C | C | C |   |   |   |   | C | C | C |   |   |   |
| 10.05 | C | C | C | C | C | C | C | C | C | C | C | C | C | C | C | C | C | C | C | C | C | C | C | C | C | C | C | C | C | C |
| 11.05 | C | C | C | C | C | C | C | C | C | C | C | C | C | C | C | C | C | C | C | C | C | C | C | C | C | C | C | C | C | C |
| 12.05 |   |   |   | C | C | C |   |   |   |   | C | C | C |   |   |   |   | C | C | C |   |   |   |   | C | C | C |   |   |   |
| 13.05 | C | C | C | C | C | C | C | C | C | C | C | C | C | C | C | C | C | C | C | C | C | C | C | C | C | C | C | C | C | C |
| 14.05 | C | C | C | C | C | C | C | C | C | C | C | C | C | C | C | C | C | C | C | C | C | C | C | C | C | C | C | C | C | C |
| 15.05 | C | C | C | C | C | C | C | C | C | C | C | C | C | C | C | C | C | C | C | C | C | C | C | C | C | C | C | C | C | C |
| 16.05 |   |   |   | C | C | C |   |   |   |   | C | C | C |   |   |   |   | C | C | C |   |   |   |   | C | C | C |   |   |   |
| 17.05 | C | C | C | C | C | C | C | C | C | C | C | C | C | C | C | C | C | C | C | C | C | C | C | C | C | C | C | C | C | C |
| 19.05 | D | D | D | D | D | D | D | D | D | D | D | D | D | D | D | D | D | D | D | D | D | D | D | D | D | D | D | D | D | D |

The fares and timetable are for travel from Dover to Calais by hovercraft. There are two fares in June, C and D.

(a) At what times can you depart from Dover and pay at the D fare?

(b) On which days of the week does the hovercraft depart at 12.05?

(c) How much does it cost for a family to travel at 08.05?

(d) What does it cost for one adult to take a car on the 15.05 sailing?

| Fares | C | D |
|---|---|---|
| Car & 1 adult | £116 | £86 |
| Car & 2 adults | £146 | £131 |
| Car & up to 4 adults | £157 | £142 |
| Family: Car & 2 adults & up to 2 children | £154 | £141 |

7. This diagram shows the number of students who are interested in Drama and Music.

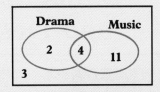

How many are interested in  (a) both Drama and Music

(b) neither Drama nor Music

(c) Drama but not Music?

8. This tree diagram shows the cars sold by Beattie's Motors.

What is missing from this diagram?

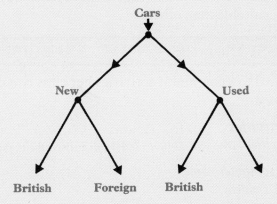

# Collecting, Organising and Describing Data

**DID YOU KNOW**  that a survey is usually done because someone wants to know the answer to a question?
Did you know that the same data can be displayed in different ways and that some of these ways are more suitable than others?

## DISCUSSION and PRACTICAL EXERCISE 21:1

• Susan was interested to know about activities her class had done. She wrote the following survey.

*Survey on Activities*

*Which of these activities have you done at least once during the past year?*

1. *Played a computer game*
2. *Recorded a video*
3. *Been to a football match*
4. *Played Trivial Pursuit*
5. *Drawn or painted a picture*
6. *Built a model*
7. *Acted in a play*
8. *Been to a concert*
9. *Been abroad*
10. *Caught a fish*

How do you think Susan might have displayed the results of her survey?
Discuss with your group or class.

• What questions would you ask if you wrote a survey about activities?
Discuss.

Write a survey on activities for your class.

# BAR-LINE GRAPHS

On a bar-line graph the height of each vertical line gives the frequency.

*Example*   Geoffrey tossed a die a number of times. He drew this bar-line graph to show his results.

This graph shows that Geoffrey threw a "one" 3 times, a "two" 4 times, a "three" twice, a "four" 3 times, a "five" 4 times and a "six" 4 times.

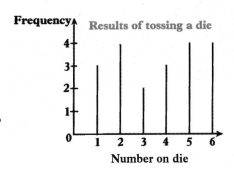

*Worked Example*   Use the previous bar-line graph to find

(a)   the number of times Geoffrey threw the die

(b)   the number of times Geoffrey got an even number.

*Answer*   (a)   We add all the frequencies together to get
$$3 + 4 + 2 + 3 + 4 + 4 = 20.$$

(b)   We add together the frequencies for "two", "four" and "six" to get
$$4 + 3 + 4 = 11.$$

*Example*   Brigid surveyed her friends about the colour of clothes they most like to wear. The results that Brigid gathered on the frequency table are shown displayed on the bar-line graph.

| Colour | Tally | Frequency |
|--------|-------|-----------|
| Red | III | 3 |
| Green | ℍℍ | 5 |
| Blue | ℍℍ III | 8 |
| White | II | 2 |
| Black | ℍℍ I | 6 |
| Other | I | 1 |

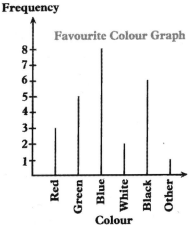

263

## EXERCISE 21:2

1. This graph shows the number of goals scored in the Division One and Division Two football matches.

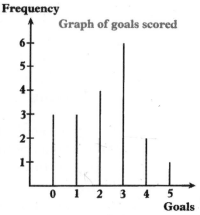

Graph of goals scored

(a) In how many matches were there no goals scored?

(b) How many matches were there altogether?

(c) In how many matches were more than 3 goals scored?

2.

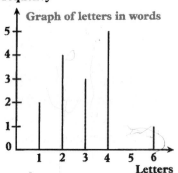

Graph of letters in words

This graph shows the number of letters in the words in the first sentence of "Robinson Crusoe".

(a) How many words have 6 letters?

(b) How many words have 5 letters?

(c) What is the most common number of letters in these words?

(d) How many words have fewer than 3 letters?

(e) How many words are there in the first sentence of "Robinson Crusoe"?

3.

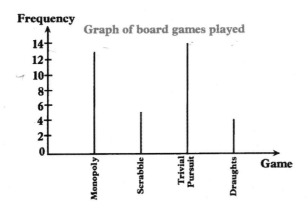

This graph shows the board games played by the students in one class.

(a) How many play Monopoly?

(b) What is the most popular game?

(c) What else can you tell from this graph?

(d) Explain why you cannot tell how many students are in the class.

4.

| Number of children | Tally | Frequency |
|---|---|---|
| 1 | \|\|\|\| | 4 |
| 2 | ~~\|\|\|\|~~ \| | 6 |
| 3 | \|\|\|\| | 4 |
| 4 | \|\| | 2 |
| 5 | \| | 1 |
| 6 | \| | 1 |

This table shows the results of Meredith's survey on the number of children in the families of some students.
Draw a bar-line graph for this data.

5. Simon surveyed the students in his class about their hobbies.
Simon wrote the results of his survey as:

INTERNATIONAL STAMP ALBUM

collecting coins  2     collecting stamps  5
reading  6              playing sport  6
playing an instrument  3     watching sport  6
making models  3

Draw a bar-line graph for this data.

6.  This list gives the number of sisters of the students in a Year 7 class.

    1  0  2  1  3  1  0  0  2  1  1  2  3  1  0  0  4  0  1  1  2  4

    Draw a bar-line graph for this data.

**Review 1**

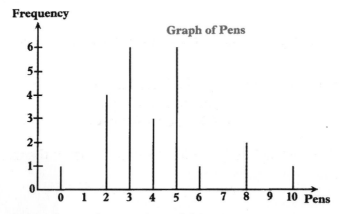

This bar-line graph shows the number of felt-tip pens in the pencil cases of the students in a class.

(a) How many students have 4 felt-tip pens?

(b) How many students have more than 5 felt-tip pens?

(c) How many students are in this class?

(d) What else does this graph tell you?

**Review 2**  Julia gathered data about the number of letters in the surnames of the teachers in her school.
This data is shown below.

|   |   |   |   |   |   |   |   |   |   |   |   |   |
|---|---|---|---|---|---|---|---|---|---|---|---|---|
| 5 | 6 | 8 | 9 | 7 | 7 | 4 | 5 | 6 | 8 | 5 | 7 | 5 |
| 3 | 8 | 4 | 7 | 6 | 6 | 8 | 6 | 9 | 8 | 5 | 6 | 3 |

Draw a bar-line graph for this data.

## DISCUSSION EXERCISE 21:3

| Page number | 1 | 2 | 3 | 4 | 5 | 6 | 7 | 8 | 9 | 10 |
|---|---|---|---|---|---|---|---|---|---|---|
| Number of advertisements | 6 | 4 | 1 | 2 | 0 | 2 | 1 | 4 | 3 | 2 |

This table gives the number of advertisements on the first 10 pages of a magazine.

How many of these pages have    (a) 2 advertisements

(b) no advertisements

(c) 1 advertisement?

Discuss how to draw a bar-line graph for the data shown in the table.

Why do you think this data might have been collected? Discuss.

## SURVEY 21:4

Collect data that can be shown on a bar-line graph.
Some ideas follow. You may use one of these or you may wish to collect data on something quite different.

Draw a bar-line graph for your data.

Ideas:    the birthmonth of the students in your class
number of people in the cars passing the main school gate
number of words in the sentences of a chapter of this book
number of recipes, on pages of a cookbook, that use two eggs
numbers obtained when a die is tossed 50 times

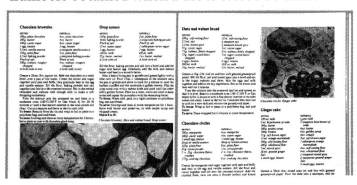

267

# GROUPING DATA

Tally charts and frequency tables can be used for data that is grouped.

*Example*   Richard collected data on the prices paid for items sold at his school's fund-raising "boot" sale. His data was:

| £4·95 | 75p  | £2·50 | £1·20 | 99p   | 50p  | £3·90 | £1·30 | £10   | £3·50 |
|-------|------|-------|-------|-------|------|-------|-------|-------|-------|
| £1·75 | £3   | £5    | 60p   | £8·50 | £2   | 50p   | 30p   | £2    | £6·99 |
| £9    | 50p  | £1    | £4·60 | £2    | £5   | £1·50 | £9    | £5·20 | £1    |
| £7·20 | £1   | £2·30 | 20p   | £4·70 | 20p  | £7·60 | 90p   | £1·50 | 70p   |
| 20p   | £4   | £9·50 | £1    | 90p   | £1·10| 50p   | £3·49 | 50p   | 25p   |

Richard put this data into the groups £0·01 to £1, £1·01 to £2, £2·01 to £3 etc. His tally chart and frequency table are shown.

| Price paid | Tally | Frequency |
|------------|-------|-----------|
| £0·01 - £1 | ℍℍ ℍℍ ℍℍ ℍℍ | 20 |
| £1·01 - £2 | ℍℍ IIII | 9 |
| £2·01 - £3 | III | 3 |
| £3·01 - £4 | IIII | 4 |
| £4·01 - £5 | ℍℍ | 5 |
| £5·01 - £6 | I | 1 |
| £6·01 - £7 | I | 1 |
| £7·01 - £8 | II | 2 |
| £8·01 - £9 | III | 3 |
| £9·01 - £10 | II | 2 |

## EXERCISE 21:5

1.  This data gives the number of pictures or posters on the walls of rooms at Millfield High School.

| 5  | 12 | 16 | 3 | 24 | 0 | 5 | 0  | 11 | 9  | 0  | 2 | 27 |
|----|----|----|---|----|---|---|----|----|----|----|---|----|
| 21 | 5  | 0  | 4 | 3  | 2 | 1 | 17 | 14 | 18 | 24 | 0 | 8  |
| 7  | 13 | 6  | 0 | 4  | 1 | 9 | 0  | 10 | 0  | 12 | 5 | 2  |

Copy and complete the following tally chart and frequency table.

| Number of Pictures or Posters | Tally | Frequency |
|---|---|---|
| 0 - 4 | | |
| 5 - 9 | | |
| 10 - 14 | | |
| 15 - 19 | | |
| 20 - 24 | | |
| 25 - 29 | | |

2.  This data gives the points scored by the people who entered a "Give a Talk" competition run by a radio station.

    29  19  25  28  26  21  37.  25  24  29  42  27
    28  32  35  41  18  20  27  48  22  17  28  29
    30  24  20  34  29  29  28  31  20  30  32  26
    24  28  30  30  20  27  28  21  23  20  27  29

    Put this data onto a tally chart and frequency table. Use the groups 15-19, 20-24, 25-29 etc.

3.  Andrew gathered data about the number of tomatoes on plants in a hothouse.

    28  62  54  29  32  47  68  17  57  48
    37  70  49  43  52  82,  61  29  38  64
    61  59  63  65  67  72  49  38  49  52
    58  65  64  59  74  91  67  68  54  57
    68  54  71  62  59  47  58  52  52  70

    (a) Why are the groups 0-9, 10-19, 20-29 etc. more suitable than the groups 0-19, 20-39, 40-59 etc.?

    (b) Put this data onto a tally chart and frequency table.

Review   Jeanette gathered data about the number of words in the first 50 sentences of the book "Living Free".

    10  21  41  5   48  13  25  38  13  25
    11  53  6   8   32  34  5   8   46  20
    55  35  21  11  30  5   13  22  24  74
    24  18  17  8   46  36  18  8   5   30
    48  5   6   6   27  42  34  16  33  7

Put this data onto a tally chart and frequency table. Use the groups 1-10, 11-20, 21-30 etc.

# FREQUENCY DIAGRAMS

A frequency diagram is used to graph grouped data.

In a frequency diagram, the vertical axis always shows the frequency.

*Example*   The list below gives the number of items bought by shoppers at a supermarket.

|    |    |    |    |    |    |    |    |    |    |    |    |    |    |
|----|----|----|----|----|----|----|----|----|----|----|----|----|----|
| 18 | 2  | 24 | 13 | 31 | 17 | 5  | 8  | 26 | 29 | 11 | 3  | 12 | 27 |
| 5  | 14 | 15 | 24 | 12 | 23 | 11 | 27 | 4  | 8  | 22 | 7  | 15 | 34 |
| 22 | 31 | 23 | 28 | 17 | 4  | 32 | 31 | 7  | 19 | 20 | 14 | 21 | 32 |
| 7  | 14 | 21 | 9  | 33 | 21 | 9  | 17 | 20 | 31 | 7  | 25 | 30 | 8  |

| Number of items | Tally | Frequency |
|:---------------:|:-----:|:---------:|
| 1-5   | 卌 I   | 6  |
| 6-10  | 卌 IIII | 9  |
| 11-15 | 卌 卌   | 10 |
| 16-20 | 卌 II  | 7  |
| 21-25 | 卌 卌   | 10 |
| 26-30 | 卌 I   | 6  |
| 31-35 | 卌 III | 8  |

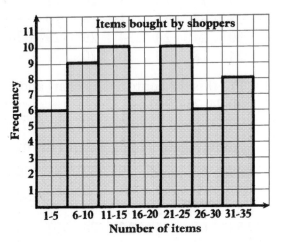

*Worked Example*   This graph shows the number of pupils in the secondary schools in a city.

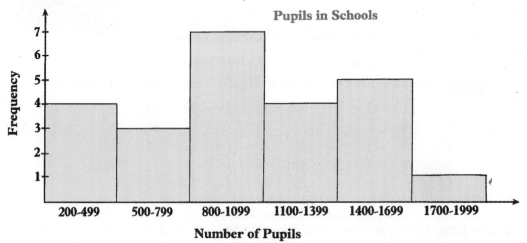

(a) How many schools have between 800 and 1099 pupils?

(b) How many schools have 1400 or more pupils?

(c) How many secondary schools are there in this city?

*Answer*   (a) 7

      (b) We add together the frequencies for the groups 1400-1699 and 1700-1999 to get $5 + 1 = 6$.

      (c) We add together all the frequencies to get
$$4 + 3 + 7 + 4 + 5 + 1 = 24.$$

## EXERCISE 21:6

**1.**

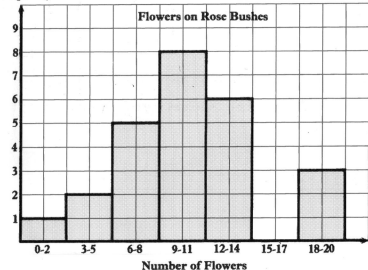

This graph shows the number of flowers on the rose bushes in Rowanway Park.

(a) How many rose bushes have between 6 and 8 flowers?

(b) How many have between 15 and 17 flowers?

(c) How many have fewer than 9 flowers?

(d) How many rose bushes are there in Rowanway Park?

2.

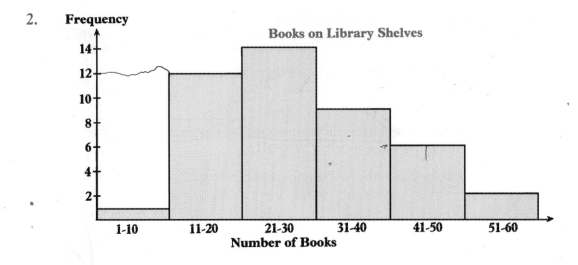

This graph shows the number of books on the shelves in the Hobbies section of a library.

(a) How many shelves have between 41 and 50 books?

(b) How many have fewer than 11 books?

(c) How many have more than 30 books?

(d) How many shelves are there in the Hobbies section of this library?

(e) Can you tell from this graph how many shelves have 20 books?

3.

| Number of Days Away | 0-4 | 5-9 | 10-14 | 15-19 | 20-24 | 25-29 |
|---|---|---|---|---|---|---|
| Frequency | 10 | 8 | 4 | 1 | 2 | 1 |

This table shows the number of days that students, from one class, were away from school during the last year.

Draw a frequency diagram for this data.

4. This data gives the number of pencils, pens etc. in the pencil cases of some students.

15   7   9   12   18   14   21   8   15   16   19   18   6   21
13   14   8   6   23   11   17   14   4   31   17   13   9   15

Group this data using the groups: 1-5, 6-10, . . .

Draw a frequency diagram for this data.

5.  Aaron did a survey on house numbers.
    This list gives the house numbers of the people that Aaron knows well.

    | 123 | 89 | 242 | 31 | 6 | 148 | 27 | 52 | 65 | 139 |
    | 22 | 19 | 158 | 210 | 91 | 74 | 10 | 1 | 232 | 101 |
    | 282 | 24 | 50 | 64 | 171 | 228 | 204 | 153 | 124 | 68 |
    | 47 | 138 | 269 | 61 | 18 | 5 | 3 | 242 | 246 | 248 |

    Group this data. Choose suitable groups.

    Draw a frequency diagram for your grouped data.

**Review 1**

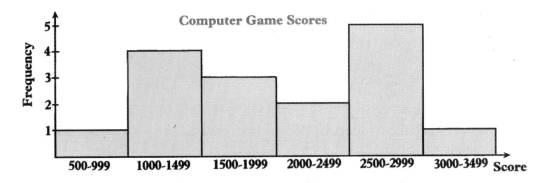

    of tries at a computer game.

    (a)  How many times did Jane score less than 1000?

    (b)  How many times did Jane score at least 2000?

    (c)  How many tries did Jane have?

    (d)  Can you tell from this graph the number of tries in which Jane's
         score was more than 1400?

**Review 2**   This data shows the number of runs scored by a member of the West
               Indies Cricket Team in Test matches.

    | 22 | 41 | 34 | 15 | 49 | 62 | 98 | 19 | 23 | 38 |
    | 38 | 59 | 113 | 47 | 71 | 86 | 68 | 54 | 101 | 45 |
    | 14 | 5 | 39 | 36 | 48 | 76 | 42 | 0 | 34 | 49 |
    | 25 | 92 | 81 | 43 | 35 | 20 | 81 | 41 | 7 | |

    Group this data. Choose suitable groups.

    Draw a frequency diagram for the grouped data.

## SURVEY 21:7

Collect and organise data that can be grouped. Graph your grouped data on a frequency diagram.
Some ideas, for data you could collect, follow. You may use one of these ideas or you could collect data on something quite different.

You might like to collect the data on a tally chart.
You could list the data first, then draw up a tally chart and frequency table.

Ideas:  number of flowers on plants in the school grounds
number of items in the school bags of students
number of digits on the pink pages of this book
goals scored by a netball team in its games in one season

## LINE GRAPHS

**Line graphs** are drawn by plotting points, then joining the points with straight lines.

*Worked Example*     This graph shows the growth of a mouse.

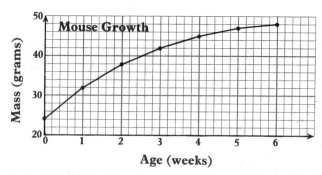

(a) What was the mass of the mouse at the end of 3 weeks?

(b) At what age did the mouse have a mass of 47 grams?

*Answer*     (a) The point plotted for 3 weeks is (3, 42).
The mass is 42 grams.

(b) The point plotted for 47 grams is (5, 47).
The mouse was 5 weeks old.

*Worked Example* — Jeremy recorded the maximum daily temperature.

| Day | Mon | Tue | Wed | Thu | Fri | Sat | Sun |
|---|---|---|---|---|---|---|---|
| Temperature (°C) | 21° | 18° | 18° | 16° | 22° | 15° | 17° |

Draw a graph for this data.

*Answer* — We plot the points (M, 21°) (T, 18°) etc., then join these points with straight lines.

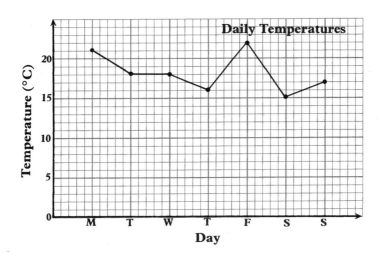

## EXERCISE 21:8

1.

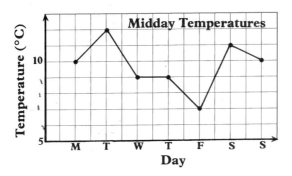

For one week, Hiroko plotted the midday temperatures. The graph she drew is shown.

275

(a) What was the midday temperature on Friday?

(b) On which day was the midday temperature 11°C?

(c) Which day had the lowest midday temperature?

(d) How much higher was the midday temperature on Saturday than on Wednesday?

2. Andrea heated a liquid, then let it cool. While it was cooling, she took the temperature every minute.

Andrea drew the graph below.

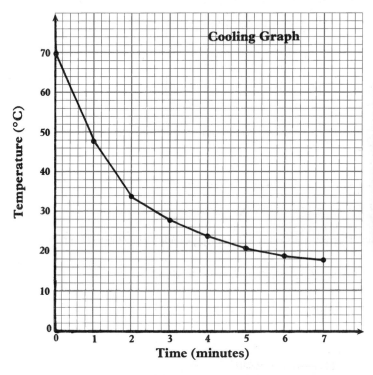

(a) What was the temperature after 1 minute?

(b) After how many minutes was the temperature 24°?

(c) To what temperature did Andrea heat the liquid?

(d) How much did the temperature drop in the first 5 minutes of cooling?

**3.**

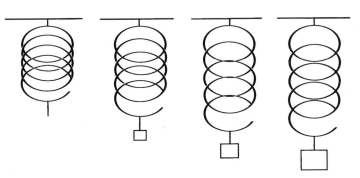

Thomas and Catherine did an experiment to find how much a spring would stretch when weights were hung from it.
They drew this graph.

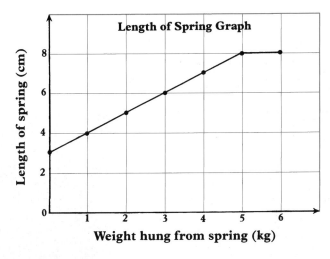

(a) What was the length of the spring when no weight was hung from it?

(b) What was the length when a 2kg weight was hung from it?

(c) How much did the spring stretch when a 2kg weight was hung from it?

**4.** Adam's group was doing a project on the weather.
Adam made and used a rain gauge to find the daily rainfall.

| Day | M | T | W | T | F | S | S |
|---|---|---|---|---|---|---|---|
| Rainfall (mm) | 0 | 7 | 0 | 5 | 4 | 2 | 6 |

Draw a graph for this.

5.  Emily began a weight-building programme in January.

| Month | J | F | M | A | M | J | J | A | S | O | N | D |
|---|---|---|---|---|---|---|---|---|---|---|---|---|
| Weight (kg) | 40 | 40 | 41 | 42 | 43 | 43 | 44 | 45 | 45 | 47 | 48 | 49 |

Draw a graph for this.

**Review 1**   William taught himself to type.
At the end of each week he tested his speed. The table shows how long it took William to type 300 words.

| Week | 1 | 2 | 3 | 4 | 5 | 6 |
|---|---|---|---|---|---|---|
| Time (minutes) | 16 | 15 | 15 | 13 | 12 | 10 |

Draw a graph.

**Review 2**   At the end of each week Laura measured the height of a plant.
This is the graph Laura drew.

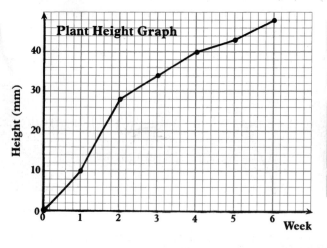

(a)  How tall was this plant at the end of the 3rd week?

(b)  How much did this plant grow in 6 weeks?

(c)  How long did it take for the plant to be 40mm tall?

(d)  How many millimetres did this plant grow in the 2nd week?

| PRACTICAL EXERCISE 21:9 |
|---|

Collect data that can be displayed on a line graph.

You could use **Exercise 21:8** for ideas. You could use one of the ideas given below. If you wish, you could collect data on something quite different.

Display your data on a line graph.

**Ideas:**    Number of students away from your maths. class each day
your percentage mark in a number of tests
time taken to do your homework on 5 or 10 nights

# MEDIAN. MODE

These photos show the number of Easter eggs given to 5 children.

These photos can be arranged as shown below.

The photos now show the number of eggs put in order from smallest to largest.

The median number of Easter eggs is the number that is in the middle photo. The median number of Easter eggs is 3.

The **median** is the middle value when a set of data is arranged in order of size.

The **mode** of a set of data is the value that occurs most often.

For instance, the mode of the number of Easter eggs received by the five children is 2.

*Worked Example*    Find the mode and the median of

(a) 2, 5, 6, 7, 7, 7, 11, 12, 15, 15, 17, 19, 19

(b) 1, 2, 3, 3, 4, 5, 5, 6, 7, 8, 9

(c) 10, 21, 15, 72, 43.

*Answer*    (a) Mode = 7.                    Median = 11

(b) There are two modes: 3 and 5.        Median = 5

(c) There is no mode.

In order, this data is 10, 15, 21, 43, 72.    Median = 21

---

In the set of data 2, 5, 8, 11, 15, 16 there are two middle values; 8 and 11.
The median is taken to be halfway between these two middle values.
That is, median $= \frac{8+11}{2}$

$= 9 \cdot 5$

---

## EXERCISE 21:10

1. Three houses in Somerset Street were sold for £98000, £89000, £99000.

   What was the median house price?

2. In an Aural Test, a group of students got these marks:

   17    16    11    16    18    12    16

   (a) What was the median mark?

   (b) What was the mode?

3.

| Wei-Hsin | John | Victoria | Rebecca | Caleb | Chien | Jeremy | Anna | Sandhya |
|----------|------|----------|---------|-------|-------|--------|------|---------|
| 1·47m | 1·57m | 1·61m | 1·39m | 1·62m | 1·65m | 1·76m | 1·53m | 1·49m |

What is the median height of these students?

4. This data gives the ages (in years) of the cats in Somerset Street.

2  5  0  7  12  5  5  8  9  1  10  6  9  3

(a) Find the median age of these cats.

(b) What is the mode of this data?

5. Andrea counted the number of items on the desks of the students in her class. Andrea's data is shown below.

7  11  10  6  5  10  5  9  12  5  7  5  7  13  16

8  10  9  8  13  4  7  5  8  9  8  7  8  5  7

(a) Find the median number of items.

(b) Find the mode.

6. The jackets on a rack were priced as follows:

| | | | | | | |
|---|---|---|---|---|---|---|
| £12·90 | £6·90 | £9·15 | £18·50 | £19·95 | £29·35 | £8·70 |
| £15·20 | £9·95 | £11·30 | £25·20 | £17·00 | £19·40 | £21·50 |
| £27·60 | £13·40 | £7·95 | £9·90 | £15·60 | £18·20 | £23·40 |

Find the median price.

7. Catherine measured the length of the corridors in one part of her school. Her data is shown below.

   18·62m    25·96m    12·54m    23·71m    27·30m    19·67m

   What is the median length of these corridors?

8. This data gives the time spent by 8 students on a project.

   1hr 40min   1hr 30min   45min   1hr   1hr 10min   50min   2hr 15min   2hr

   (a) What was the median time spent?

   (b) What was the mode?

**Review 1**    This data gives the prices of the cars for sale at Pitman Motors.

   £5450   £7199   £3849   £4795   £5267   £3680   £4275
   £4695   £4295   £3550   £6999   £5999   £6295   £3685
   £3599   £3295   £4290   £5650   £3250   £3699   £3749

   (a) Find the median price.

   (b) Find the mode.

**Review 2**    Tina measured the length of the pencils in her pencil case.
Her data was: 96mm, 168mm, 89mm, 154mm, 86mm, 95mm, 89mm, 142mm.

   (a) Find the median length of Tina's pencils.

   (b) Find the mode.

## DISCUSSION EXERCISE and SURVEY 21:11

Choose a theme such as:　　sport
　　　　　　　　　　　　　your school
　　　　　　　　　　　　　traffic
　　　　　　　　　　　　　pollution
　　　　　　　　　　　　　other countries
　　　　　　　　　　　　　the school neighbourhood
　　　　　　　　　　　　　school sports day

**Discuss** what data could be collected on this theme.

Collect this data.

Decide on the best way to show your findings.
You could use one or more of:　　graphs
　　　　　　　　　　　　　　　　tables
　　　　　　　　　　　　　　　　illustrated talk
　　　　　　　　　　　　　　　　video
　　　　　　　　　　　　　　　　wall mural
　　　　　　　　　　　　　　　　poster
　　　　　　　　　　　　　　　　booklet

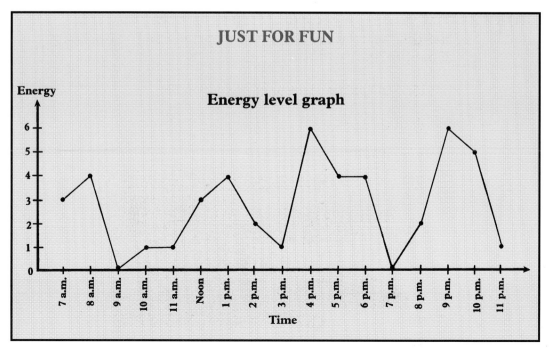

JUST FOR FUN

Energy level graph

Rate your energy level at different times of the day.
You could use a scale such as that below.

| | |
|---|---|
| 0 | no energy |
| 1 | little energy |
| 2 | less than average energy |
| 3 | average energy |
| 4 | above average energy |
| 5 | lots of energy |
| 6 | full of energy |

Plot your energy levels on a graph.
Join the points with straight lines.

Instead of drawing a graph for energy level you could draw a graph for your
mood. Your ratings could go from 0 for very sad to 5 for very happy.

**DID YOU KNOW**    that in the 17th century a gambler asked the
mathematician Blaise Pascal how often two sixes
would come up in 24 tosses of two dice?

## DISCUSSION EXERCISE and GAME 22:1

- Coins, dice and cards are used in gambling. They are also used in
  non-gambling games.
  What games do you know that use dice or coins or cards?
  **Discuss** with your group or class.

  Play one of these games or play the following game.

● **COINS: a game for a group.**

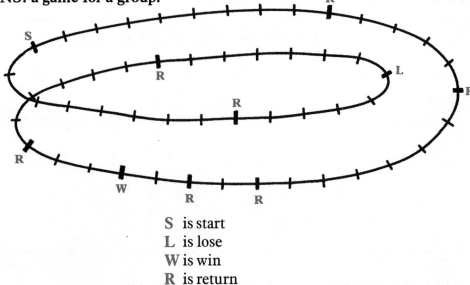

S  is start
L  is lose
W is win
R  is return

Equipment:   A curve, like that shown, drawn up on a piece of paper.
             (The diagram should be about four times as large as that shown.)

             A different coloured counter for each player.

             Two coins.

The Play:    The players begin with their counters at **S**.

             The players take turns to toss the two coins and make the following
             moves:
                 if two heads come up, move 2 spaces clockwise
                 if one head comes up, move 1 space clockwise
                 if no heads come up, move 2 spaces anticlockwise

Rules:       If a player's counter is moved to one of the places marked **R**, the
             counter must be returned to **S**.

             The winner is the first player to land on **W**.

             If a player's counter lands on **L**, this player is no longer in the
             game.

● Make up a game that uses dice or coins.
  Give your game to other groups to play.

# HOW LIKELY

| DISCUSSION EXERCISE 22:2 |
| --- |

- Copy these 3 boxes. Put each of the events 1 to 10 into one of them.

| **WILL HAPPEN** | **MIGHT HAPPEN** | **WILL NOT HAPPEN** |
| --- | --- | --- |
|  |  |  |

Discuss which boxes you put the events in and why.

1.  *A bird will land in the school grounds today.* w

2.  *A baby will be born somewhere tomorrow.* M

3.  *A pig will fly past the window.* N

4.  *A boy will ride down the street at midnight.* w

5.  *The sun will rise tomorrow.* M

6.  *A person will walk from London to Brighton in 5 minutes.*

7.  *A person in your class will be sick tomorrow.*

8.  *If you toss a die it will be a six.*

9.  *It will rain on Christmas Day this year.*

10. *Someone in your family will go shopping tomorrow.*

- Look at the events you have written in the MIGHT HAPPEN box. Which
  of these is — very likely
              — likely
              — unlikely
              — very unlikely to happen?
Discuss.

## INVESTIGATION 22:3

**HOW LIKELY**

"It is more likely that a family with 2 children will have a boy and a girl rather than 2 boys," said Carl.

"It is more likely that a drawing pin will land on its back than on its point," said Jim.

"If I drop a counter onto this board it is more likely to land on a line than in a space," said Shushila.

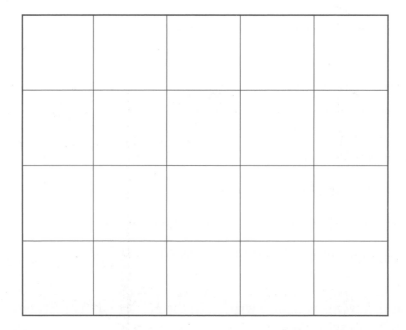

Make a prediction like Carl's, Jim's or Shushila's.
**Investigate** to see if it is true.

We can say that events are either    certain
                           or   very likely
                           or   likely
                           or   unlikely
                           or   very unlikely
                           or   impossible.

*Examples*     If today is Monday the 3rd of June;

it is certain tomorrow will be Tuesday

it is very likely there will be cloud sometime today

it is likely it will be sunny sometime tomorrow

it is unlikely to rain all day tomorrow and the next day

it is very unlikely to snow tomorrow

it is impossible that tomorrow will be Friday.

## EXERCISE 22:4

1. Decide if each of the following **might happen, will happen** or **will not happen.**

(a) You will turn into a frog tomorrow.

(b) A plane will fly from Heathrow airport tomorrow.

(c) You will be away from school sometime next month.

(d) A famous person will visit you tomorrow.

(e) You will have a drink sometime next week.

(f) Some people in the world will cry today.

(g) You will smile sometime next week.

2. Which colour is the spinner most likely to stop on?

(a)
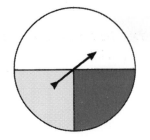

(b)
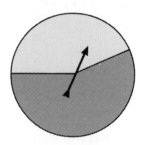

(c)
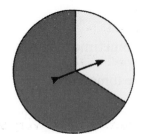

(d)
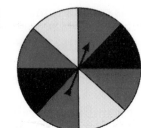

3. Which of the events, A or B, is more likely?

(a) A: You will see a red car tomorrow.
B: You will see a pink bus tomorrow.

(b) A: You will see a lorry tomorrow.
B: You will see a blue lorry tomorrow.

(c) A: A baby will be born in a plane tomorrow.
B: You will have some food next week.

(d) A: School will be open on Christmas Day.
B: A mouse will squeak tonight.

4. Put these events in order of likelihood. Put the most likely first.

A. A lion will eat you tomorrow.
B. The sun will rise tomorrow.
C. The Prime Minister will visit you this year.
D. You will fly to Hollywood some day.
E. Someone in your class will be sick tomorrow.
F. You will eat breakfast tomorrow.

**5.**

| Colour | Number |
|--------|--------|
| Red | 18 |
| Green | 12 |
| Blue | 6 |
| Yellow | 21 |

This table shows the number of sweets of each colour in a packet.

I put my hand in the packet and take a sweet.

(a) Which colour sweet am I most likely to take out? Why?

(b) Which colour sweet am I least likely to take out? Why?

**6.** Decide if each of these is **certain, very likely, likely, unlikely, very unlikely or impossible.**

(a) The next 50 babies born in London will all be girls.

(b) The day after Monday will be Tuesday.

(c) A seal will drive a car down your street.

(d) Someone in your class will eat some fruit tomorrow.

(e) Someone in your class will be late to school next week.

**Review 1** Put these events in order of likelihood. Put the most likely first.

A. A counter dropped on this board will land on red.

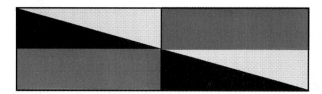

B. The stars will shine tonight.
C. A dog will turn into a rabbit.
D. Someone in your class will write the word "the" tomorrow.

**Review 2**

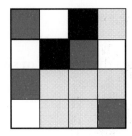

This is a board used in a game.

(a) Which colour are players most likely to land on? Why?

(b) Which colour are players least likely to land on? Why?

**Review 3**  Decide if each of these is **certain, very likely, likely, unlikely, very unlikely** or **impossible.**

(a) Someone will visit your house in the next week.

(b) A shopper at your local supermarket will buy smarties today.

(c) You will read 50 books this week.

(d) A polar bear will give you a kiss tomorrow.

(e) It will get dark tonight.

## EVENS

### DISCUSSION EXERCISE 22:5

"Heads or tails?" asked Cushla.
"I want heads," said Karen. "It wins more often than tails."

Is Karen right? **Discuss.**

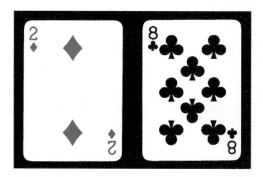

Does a pack of cards have the same number of red as black cards? If you take one card from the pack, is it more likely to be red or black? **Discuss.**

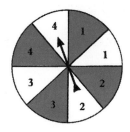

Caleb and Jasmine played a game with this spinner.
When the spinner stopped on red, Caleb moved his counter the number shown.
When it landed on white Jasmine moved her counter the number shown.

Did Caleb and Jasmine have the same chance of winning? **Discuss.**

What if Caleb and Jasmine had used one of these spinners? **Discuss.**

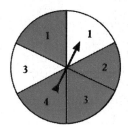

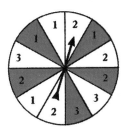

There is an **even chance** of an event happening if there is the same chance of it happening as not happening.

*Example*   If we toss a coin, there is an even chance it will be a head.

There is a **less than even chance** of an event happening if it is less likely to happen than not happen.

*Example*   One card is drawn from a pack of cards. There is a less than even chance it will be a spade.

There is a **better than even chance** of an event happening if it is more likely to happen than not happen.

*Example*   A die is tossed. There is a better than even chance that a number greater than two will be tossed.

---

**EXERCISE 22:6**

---

1. Celie had a bag of sweets. There were 17 red and 17 green sweets in the bag. Celie took one. Did she have an even chance of getting a red sweet?

2. At a fair, a stall sold balloons. There were 47 blue and 29 yellow ones. One of the balloons burst. Is there an even, less than even or better than even chance it will be yellow?

3. Decide if the following events have an even, less than even or better than even chance of happening.

   (a) Jason will get a head when he tosses a coin.

   (b) Melanie will get a 5 when she tosses a die.

   (c) Four children in a family will all be girls.

   (d) Ismael will get a number greater than 1 when he tosses a die.

   (e) The next baby born will be a boy.

   (f) The next card Andrew takes from a pack will be a diamond.

4. Is there an even, less than even or better than even chance of these spinners stopping on red? Why?

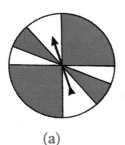
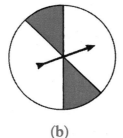
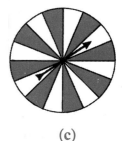

(a)                    (b)                    (c)

5. This table shows the pets in a "Best Pet Competition". Each pet was given a lucky number. The lucky number was drawn out of a hat.

| Pet | Number |
|---------|--------|
| Dog | 25 |
| Cat | 15 |
| Rabbit | 7 |
| Hamster | 3 |

Is there an even, less than even or better than even chance of

(a) a dog winning

(b) a cat winning?


**Review 1** Decide if these events have an even, less than even or better than even chance of happening.

(a) A glass will break when it is dropped onto concrete.

(b) The next baby born will be a girl.

(c) Todd will get the ace of clubs when he chooses one card from a pack.


**Review 2** A class captain is to be chosen. The names given in the table were put in a hat. The teacher took one out.

| Name | Boy/Girl | Age |
|-------|----------|-----|
| Ahmed | Boy | 12 |
| Sarah | Girl | 11 |
| Blair | Boy | 11 |
| Helen | Girl | 11 |

Is there an even, less than even or better than even chance that

(a) a boy will be chosen

(b) an 11-year-old will be chosen

(c) an 11-year-old boy will be chosen?

# DISCUSSION and PRACTICAL EXERCISE 22:7

● Make a spinner like this one.

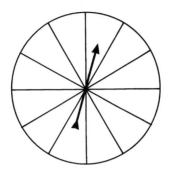

Colour it red, blue and yellow so that there is an even chance the spinner will stop on blue.

● Make another spinner using green, yellow and blue. Colour it so that there is a better than even chance the spinner will stop on green.

● Think of stalls at a fair. How likely is it you would win something on one of these?
Which stall do you think you are most likely to win on?
**Discuss.**

● Each class at Rockhampton School had to make up an idea for a stall at the school fair. Sheena's class made up this.

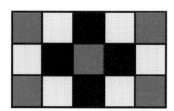

A coin is dropped onto this board. If it lands in a red square the player wins a prize.
Each player pays 10p a go.
Do you think the stall will make money for the school? **Discuss.**

● Make up an idea for a stall at a school fair. Test to see if your stall would make money for the school.

# FAIR AND UNFAIR

<table>
<tr><td>**GAME** 22:8</td></tr>
</table>

**LAST OUT** — a game for 4 players.

**Preparation**   Trace these onto thin card. Cut out and put together to make a spinner. You could use a toothpick or matchstick to join the two parts.

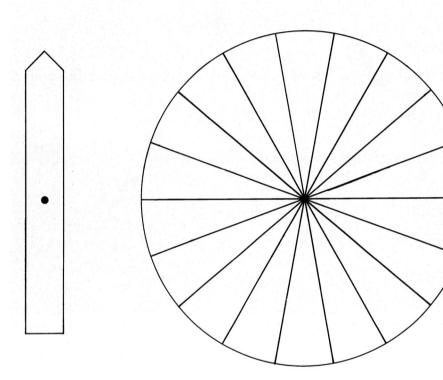

Colour   —   9 parts one colour
         —   4 parts another colour
         —   3 parts another colour
         —   2 parts another colour.

**Equipment:**   the spinner you have just made
              4 counters, one for each colour you have on the spinner.

*continued . . .*

. . . *from previous page*

**The play:** Put the counters in a bag. Take one counter (without looking). This is your colour on the spinner.

Spin the spinner. If it stops on your colour you are out of the game.

The last person left is the winner.

## DISCUSSION EXERCISE 22:9

* Why is **Game 22:8** not a fair game? Discuss.
  How could you make it fair? Discuss.

* "For a game to be fair, everyone has to have a chance of winning," said Pru.
  "I think everyone has to have the *same* chance of winning," said Jafar.

  Discuss what Pru and Jafar said.

- Anton, Fiona and Kirsty played a game of **TOSS 6.** The first to toss 6 ten times won.
  Anton's cube had 5, 6, 6, 3, 4, 2, on it.
  Fiona's cube had 4, 4, 4, 6, 6, 6.
  Kirsty's cube had 6, 3, 4, 1, 1, 2 on it.
  Is this a fair game? Discuss.

  How could you make this game fair? Discuss

- Emily and Alice made up a game. A die was used.
  One of the rules was, if Alice tossed a 1 she was allowed another turn, if Emily tossed a 2 she was allowed another two turns.

  Is this game fair? Discuss.

  How could you make this game fair? Discuss.

---

## PRACTICAL EXERCISE 22:10

**Work In Groups**

Make up a game called *"Highest Number Wins."* Use counters in a bag, dice or a board with different coloured squares.

Give your game to another group to play. Decide if the game your group played is fair or not and why.

## JUST FOR FUN

*Step 1*    Deal 15 cards, face up, in three piles. You will have 5 cards in each pile.

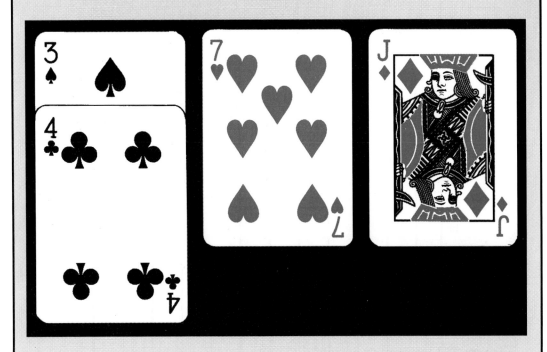

*Step 2*    Ask your neighbour to secretly remember one of the cards.

*Step 3*    Ask your neighbour to tell you which pile the secret card is in.

*Step 4*    Pick up all three piles, one after the other, making sure the secret card is in the middle pile.

*Step 5*    Repeat **steps 1, 3 and 4** twice.

*Step 6*    Deal the cards, face up, in a row.
The eighth card you deal is the secret card.

This trick can be done with other numbers of cards. **Investigate.**
(Hint: The secret card is the eighth card only if 15 cards are dealt. The cards must be dealt three times only if 15 cards are dealt.)

1. Satweer did a survey on the star sign of the Year 7 students at Brightwater School.

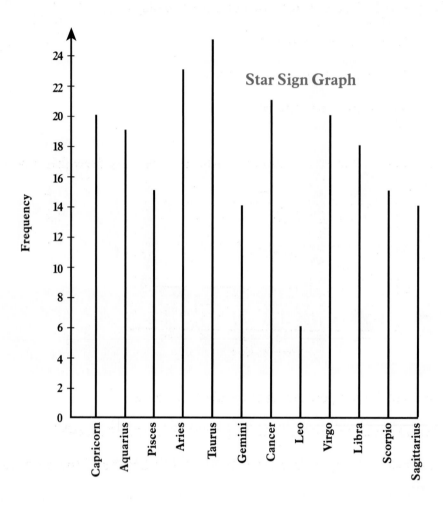

(a) How many students had star sign Gemini?

(b) How many had star sign Pisces?

(c) The most common star sign is Taurus. Which is the least common?

(d) Which star sign has the same number of students as Sagittarius?

(e) How many students were in Satweer's survey?

(f) Seventeen other students had the same star sign as Satweer. What is Satweer's star sign?

2. For each of these, decide if it **will happen** **will not happen** **might happen**

   (a) Leaves will fall from trees in autumn.

   (b) Shelley will win the next game of tennis she plays.

   (c) You will get a letter tomorrow.

   (d) You will see a live dinosaur next week.

   (e) There will be showers tomorrow.

3. Sasha and Joanne heated a liquid for 1 minute, then they drew this graph.

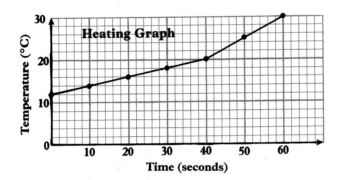

   (a) What was the temperature at the end of 1 minute?

   (b) After how many seconds of heating was the temperature 24°C?

   (c) What was the temperature of the liquid before Sasha and Joanne began heating it?

   (d) By how much did the temperature rise in the first 30 seconds?

4. Put these events in order of likelihood. Put the most likely first.

   > A rubber ball will bounce when dropped.
   > A glass will break when dropped.
   > A car will drive into your classroom tomorrow.
   > A fish will walk across your school grounds tonight.
   > A pop concert will be given somewhere in England this week.
   > Someone in Britain will have a 105th birthday tomorrow.

5. Mrs Blake's class got these marks for practical work.

| 21 | 18 | 15 | 27 | 19 | 14 | 9 | 21 | 16 | 24 | 5 | 18 |
|---|---|---|---|---|---|---|---|---|---|---|---|
| 14 | 23 | 21 | 26 | 12 | 8 | 20 | 19 | 21 | 10 | 4 | 14 |

(a) Write these marks in order, from the smallest to the largest.

(b) What is the median mark?

(c) The mode is 21. Explain what this means.

(d) Copy and complete this tally chart.

| Mark | Tally | Frequency |
|---|---|---|
| 1-5 | | |
| 6-10 | | |
| 11-15 | | |
| 16-20 | | |
| 21-25 | | |
| 26-30 | | |

(e) Copy and complete this frequency diagram.

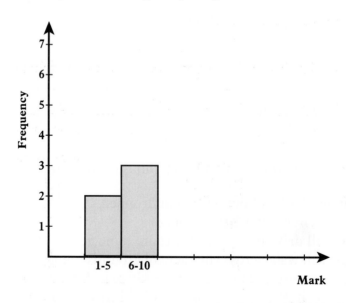

6. Decide if these events have an even, less than even or better than even chance of happening.

   (a) Charlie will spin red with this spinner.

   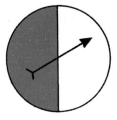

   (b) Marion will toss a 5 or a 6 with a die.

   (c) Sita will take a red marble out of this bag.

   (d) Luigi will break his leg tomorrow.

   (e) Theresa will go to sleep tonight.

   (f) Andy will toss a head with a coin.

7. Kate collected data about the colour of cars passing the school gate.

   | Colour of cars passing school gate. | | |
   |---|---|---|
   | Day: Monday | Time: 10 a.m. to 10:30 am | |
   | Colour | Tally | Frequency |
   | Grey | TTTT TTTT III | 13 |
   | White | TTTT TTTT | 10 |
   | Black | III | 3 |
   | Red | TTTT II | 7 |
   | Green | III | 3 |
   | Blue | IIII | 4 |
   | Other | II | 2 |

Draw a bar-line graph for this data.

8. Decide if each of these events is **certain, very likely, likely, unlikely, very unlikely** or **impossible.**

    (a) Claire will toss 10 heads with a coin, one after the other.

    (b) Three people in your class will have birthdays on the same day.

    (c) There will be snow at the North Pole today.

    (d) It will be sunny five days in a row in July.

    (e) Klara takes one card from a pack of cards. It will be a heart.

    (f) A high jumper will jump 10 metres.

    (g) There will be a traffic jam on the M25 on a bank holiday weekend.

    (h) The day after Monday will be Tuesday.

9.

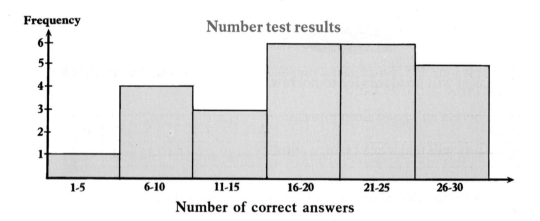

People being interviewed for a job were given a number test with 30 questions. This graph shows the number of correct answers given by these people.

    (a) How many gave between 26 and 30 correct answers?

    (b) How many gave more than 20 correct answers?

    (c) How many got one-half or fewer of the questions correct?

    (d) How many people were interviewed?

10. Alicia, Maryanne, Mike and Casey played this game. Each player chose a colour. Alicia chose red, Mike blue, Maryanne green and Casey yellow.

    12 red counters, 8 blue counters, 5 green counters and 3 yellow counters were put in a bag.

    Players took turns at taking a counter out of the bag. The first player to get two counters of their colour was the winner.

    Explain why this game is unfair.

11. Part of Jason's P.E. programme was to work at improving the distance he could throw a cricket ball.

| Day | 1 | 2 | 3 | 4 | 5 | 6 | 7 | 8 | 9 | 10 |
|---|---|---|---|---|---|---|---|---|---|---|
| Greatest distance (m) | 31 | 32 | 34 | 33 | 41 | 39 | 39 | 42 | 44 | 45 |

    Draw a line graph for this.

12. Some of the squares on this board are red, some are black, some are grey and the rest are pink.

A counter is dropped onto the board.
There is an even chance the counter will land on red.
The counter is more likely to land on grey than on black.
The counter is less likely to land on pink than on black.

(a) Copy and colour the board.

(b) How many squares are black?

# INDEX